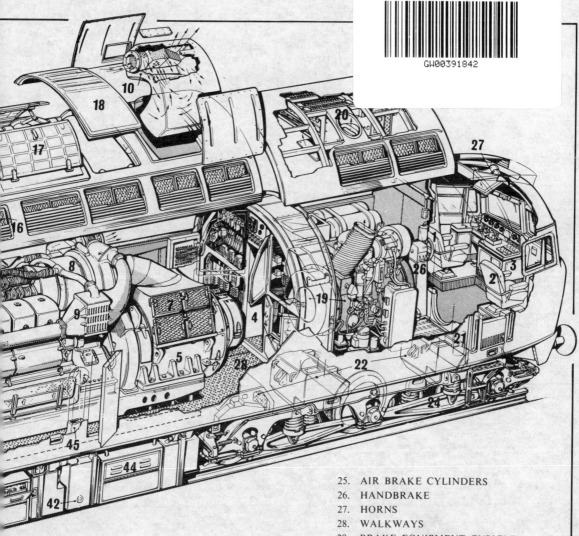

1. CHARGE AIR INTERCOOLERS
2. SILENCER AND EXHAUST OUTLET
3. LUBRICATING OIL HEAT EXCHANGER
4. LUBRICATING OIL FILTER
5. RADIATOR FANS
6. "BRUSH" ELECTRIC MOTORS FOR FAN DRIVE
7. "SERCK" ROOF MOUNTED RADIATORS
8. AIR FILTER PANELS
9. TRANSLUCENT FIBREGLASS HINGED ROOF DOORS
10. TRANSLUCENT FIBREGLASS COVERS
11. "SPANNER" TRAIN HEATING BOILER
12. BOILER FLUE OUTLET
13. FIRE EXTINGUISHER CO_2 BOTTLES
14. "BRUSH" TRACTION MOTORS
15. RESILIENT GEARWHEEL
16. "COMMONWEALTH" THREE-AXLE CAST STEEL BOGIES

25. AIR BRAKE CYLINDERS
26. HANDBRAKE
27. HORNS
28. WALKWAYS
29. BRAKE EQUIPMENT CUBICLE
30. AIR COMPRESSOR
31. COMPRESSOR AFTER COOLER
32. BREAKFAST COOKER
33. WASHBASIN
34. TOILET
35. TRACTION MOTOR AIR DUCTING
36. TRACTION MOTOR BLOWER
37. "NORTHEY" RE125. EXHAUSTERS
38. AIR RESERVOIRS
39. RADIATOR HEADER TANK
40. RADIATOR DRAIN TANK
41. MAIN FUEL TANK
42. BOILER WATER TANKS
43. FUEL OIL ENGINE FEED TANK
44. BATTERIES
45. LINE-SIDE WATER FILLER DUCTING
46. RESISTOR UNITS

CLASS 47 DIESELS

CLASS 47 DIESELS

A.T.H. Tayler, W.G.F. Thorley & T.J. Hill

LONDON

IAN ALLAN LTD

First published 1979

ISBN 0 7110 0915 5

Design by Robert C. Wilcockson

© T. J. Hill, A.T. H. Tayler,
and the late W. G. F. Thorley, 1979

Published by Ian Allan Ltd, Shepperton, Surrey;
and printed in the United Kingdom by
Ian Allan Printing Ltd

Contents

Preface

There is a tendency for enthusiasts to regard a large class of locomotives with a jaundiced eye and the fact that members appear everywhere tends to the view that interest is less than might be the case if a multiplicity of types is employed. It was with some degree of trepidation that I received the invitation from my old and late friend W. G. F. (Bill) Thorley to assist in the preparation of this book.

Bill was fighting an illness which was slowly weakening him bodily when this task commenced and I am sorry to say that he passed away at the very beginning of 1976. At that time, together with another colleague, we had completed most of the manuscript and had decided on many of the illustrations needed to go with the text, even if they were not all in a state suitable for the publisher.

Even though a 'steam' man through his training and experience, Bill took the change of motive power in his stride and had a good understanding of its capabilities, its shortcomings, advantages and disadvantages. He was a thoroughly practical engineer and this is exemplified in [his] own book *A Breath of Steam*, and he was collecti[ng] material together for a second volume when fate overto[ok] him. It was to be a personal account and it is our loss th[at] only he could have put the story of his later experien[ce] into words.

This book is largely his work and where he did n[ot] actually write the text, the ideas for the material were [his] and he edited the manuscript, a task which beca[me] increasingly difficult for him physically as the book to[ok] shape. It is hoped that this story about the largest sin[gle] class of locomotives on British Railways fulfils [its] purpose in its attempt to present an account of th[eir] development, from their inception to their half-life gene[ral] overhaul.

Much of this book would not have been possi[ble] without the help of friends and colleagues in Brit[ish] Railways, Brush Electrical Machines, Sulzer Broth[ers] and Vickers. Thanks must also go to Jean Baker w[ho] typed the original manuscript.

A.T.H.T , January 1979

1 How the Fleet was Founded

The year 1962 was notable in the annals of the development of higher-powered diesel traction for line service on British Railways. The performance of no less than three large prototype diesel-electric locomotives, all designed and built by leading British manufacturers, was being evaluated on BR main lines. The three were the Brush *Falcon* of 2,800bhp with two quick-running engines, the Birmingham Railway Carriage and Wagon/Sulzer/AEI *Lion* of 2,750bhp and the English Electric DP2 of 2,700bhp each with one medium-speed engine. All had the Co-Co wheel arrangement and four-stroke pressure charged and charge-cooled engines (with cooling of charge air). Meanwhile, on the East Coast main line, the Deltics were beginning to aggregate some impressive mileage at high speeds, the last of the fleet having entered service in April 1962.

In the midst of this competitive testing, the 2,750bhp Co-Co machine from the works of Brush at Loughborough made its debut in late 1962 with rather less than the usual stir of enthusiastic interest which heralds the appearance of a prototype locomotive in this country. Disenchantment had already been expressed in some quarters with the performance of the 2,300 and 2,500bhp machines of the 1Co-Co1 wheel arrangement then being produced in large numbers in British Railway workshops. To enable these 1Co-Co1 locomotives to run over a wide geographical area, involving most secondary as well as all main routes, they were equipped with eight axles in order to keep individual driving axle loads in the region of 18½ to 19 ton, with about 12½ ton on the two-wheeled trucks at each end of the locomotive. Considerable evidence was available from sources abroad to lead to the conclusion that the track was subjected to higher stresses when the comparatively small-diameter wheel of diesel or electric locomotives passed over it than from the large-diameter driving wheels of steam locomotives carrying the same load. In order to limit stresses, particularly in the rail head, it was considered that the ratio of axle load P in tons to wheel diameter D in feet should desirably not exceed 4.5, a figure which has since been increased from further experience accumulated in

Right: Ornate buildings and oil lamps frame D1728 as it passes Wadborough near Worcester on the 11.00 from Liverpool Lime Street on 7 March 1965. / *A. A. Vickers*

this country and abroad in the intervening years. In the event the requirement was relaxed slightly, since practical considerations arising out of the extremely restrictive British loading gauge meant that wheel diameter for all practical purposes had to be limited to 45in with new tyres, and so a P : D ratio of 5 was finally accepted. It can be seen, therefore, that the design of a locomotive with a heavy medium-speed prime mover presented many difficulties and taxed the ingenuity of the locomotive designers.

Locomotives having the lCo-Col wheel arrangement suffered from other disadvantages. The 2,300/2,500bhp locomotives built by BR had a length over buffers of 67ft 11in, whilst those designed and built by English Electric were even longer at 69ft 6in. There was a considerable overhang on curves, although the effects of this were minimised by attaching the buffing and draw gear to the bogies and not to the underframe, as is the more normal arrangement. Despite the leading trucks, the minimum radius curve that could be negotiated without gauge widening varied from 5 to 4.5 chains. More

restrictive, however, was the large radius of 24 chain required in a vertical concave curve for safe negotiatio by a BR-designed lCo-Col locomotive, due largely to th adoption of a bogie design without secondary suspensio and large turntable-type bearings. Many vertical curve found in the humps of marshalling yards had been built t a smaller radius and required reshaping before these long wheelbase locomotives could run over them without ris of derailment or damage to themselves.

These facts were well known to and fully appreciate by the Eastern Region representatives who attended meeting of high level motive power and other officers a BR Marylebone Headquarters in mid-1959. The batch o lCo-Col locomotives then about to emerge from BI workshops had not as yet been allocated to a Region an much pressure was brought to bear upon the Easter Region to take these units in order to hasten the demise o steam to that Region. However, the ER officers advance skilled arguments as to why the locomotives wer unacceptable to them. There is little doubt that the clos liaison which had existed between Brush and the Easter Region since the ordering and commissioning of th Mirrlees-engined 1,250bhp A1A-A1A locomotives (no Class 31) had resulted in firm support from a majo Region for Brush in their endeavour to produce a highe horsepower locomotive within reasonable weight limits loading gauge and other constraints. Arguments in favou of working several locomotives of modest horsepower i multiple as widely practised in America had been pursue at great length in this country, but it was evident that there were sufficient operating rosters providing continuous and heavy work in the field of mineral movement for which a single powerful locomotive was the cheapest solution.

The problem confronting Brush was the development of a powerful locomotive which would be shorter and lighter than the existing 2,500bhp units, thus enabling the outer two-wheeled trucks of the 1Co-Co1 design to be eliminated. Moreover, a shorter, lighter total adhesion locomotive, even of the same installed horsepower, would produce more power at the drawbar and hence greater tractive capacity for the operating department. The desired object was achieved by departing from an orthodox design of underframe and adopting an integral monocoque design, on the lines of that widely used in aircraft construction. Briefly, the monocoque principle provides for a stressed skin body structure consisting of thin sheet metal, strengthened by transverse and longitudinal members, to be built up as an integral unit with the underframe. The stressed skin arrangement creates a very strong resistance to buffing loads and occupies less space. Theoretical calculations to determine the resistance to sustain various loads, including buckling, are extremely complex and it is usual to subject a prototype structure to strain gauge tests.

Allied to the monocoque form of body construction were the Commonwealth six-wheeled bogies, already giving good service on the Brush prototype locomotive *Falcon*. To power the new locomotive, the Sulzer 12LDA28-C twin-bank 12-cylinder engine, rated at 2,750bhp at 800rpm, was available, being the development of the 2,500bhp engine fitted to the earlier 1Co-Co1 locomotives and already installed in the *Lion*. Once again the initiative shown by British private locomotive builders in anticipating the demand for more powerful locomotives and which had resulted in production of *Falcon* and *Lion*, had provided the opportunity to gain valuable initial experience in day-to-day operation of the most powerful medium-speed engine available for traction purposes in this country.

Thus was evolved the Class 47, as it came to be universally known throughout BR within the locomotive classification scheme adopted in 1968.

During the period from November 1962, when the first Class 47 made its appearance, to April 1968 when the last one entered service, no fewer than 512 of them emerged from the Loughborough works of Brush and BR Crewe workshops respectively. Although there have been fleets of steam locomotives nominally of the same design which reached greater totals on BR — eg 772 Class 4F 0-6-0 on the Midland, S&DJR and LMS Railways; or 842 Class 8F 2-8-0 Stanier locomotives on the LMS and later BR — their entry into service was spread over a much greater number of years, which was a good thing from the point of view of design development. Later the five Class 47 locomotives fitted with Sulzer engines having their cylinders in V formation were redesignated by BR as Class 48, but when the V engines were subsequently replaced these five reverted to Class 47. A graphic representation of the rate of entry of Class 47 locomotives into service is shown in Fig 1.

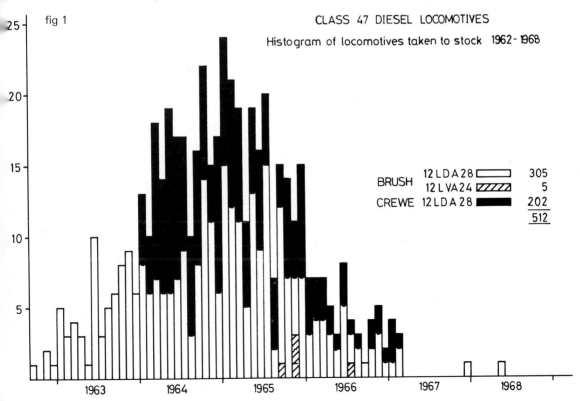

fig 1

CLASS 47 DIESEL LOCOMOTIVES

Histogram of locomotives taken to stock 1962 - 1968

BRUSH	12 LDA 28	305
	12 LVA 24	5
CREWE	12 LDA 28	202
		512

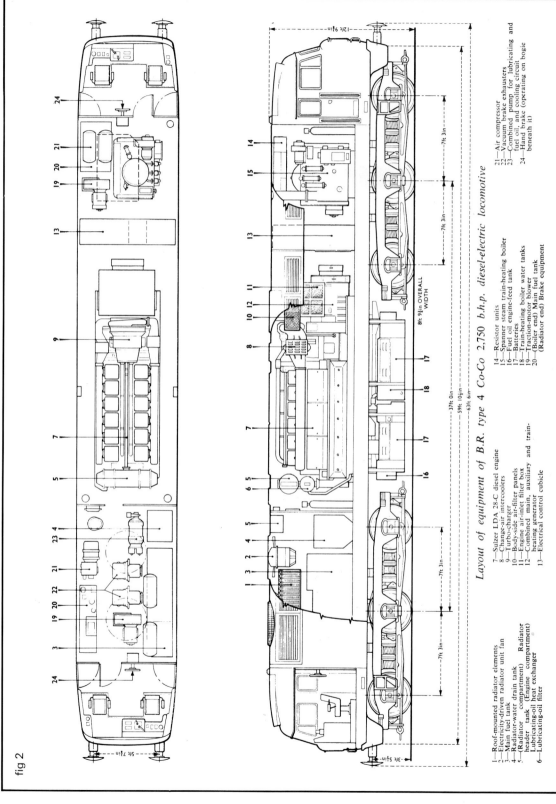

Layout of equipment of B.R. type 4 Co-Co 2,750 b.h.p. diesel-electric locomotive

1—Roof-mounted radiator elements
2—Electricity-driven radiator unit fan
3—Main fuel tank
4—Radiator-water drain tank
5—(Radiator compartment) Radiator
   header tank (Engine compartment)
   Lubricating-oil heat exchanger
6—Lubricating-oil filter

7—Sulzer LDA 28-C diesel engine
8—Change-air intercoolers
9—Turbo-charger
10—Body-side air-filter panels
11—Engine air-inlet filter box
12—Combined main, auxiliary and train-
    heating generator
13—Electrical control cubicle

14—Resistor units
15—Spanner steam train-heating boiler
16—Fuel oil engine-feed tank
17—Batteries
18—Train-heating boiler water tanks
19—Traction-motor blower
20—(Boiler end) Main fuel tank
    (Radiator end) Brake equipment

21—Air compressor
22—Vacuum brake exhausters
23—Combined pump for lubricating and
    fuel oil, and cooling circuit
24—Hand brake (operating on bogie
    beneath it)

fig 2

The arrangement drawing, Fig 2, together with the endpaper shows outline appearance and leading dimensions of the locomotive and the way in which the main power equipment and auxiliary machinery was positioned in the body to give maximum accessibility and an acceptable weight distribution. Even so the weight in working order of the first batch of 20 came out at 116 ton 8cwt, with 19 ton 15cwt on the outer axle of No 2 end bogie. Thus, with a wheel diameter of 3ft 9in, the desirable P/D ratio of 5.0 was slightly exceeded. In the fullness of time there were to be no less than 10 variations of the basic Class 47 design (11 if the five locomotives fitted with the Sulzer 12LVA24 engine are included), but the total weight in working order of only four of them was greater than that of the prototype locomotives and the total weight in working order of the heaviest was less than two tons more than the prototype.

Above: D1500 as originally built. / *Sulzer Bros (UK) Ltd*

The monocoque principle of body construction is well illustrated in Fig 3, which shows the welded framework to which the steel body sheeting is also welded, the whole assembly being integral with the underframe. Traction loads are transferred from the bogie pivots to the body sides by fabricated steel cross stretchers of box section. The lifting and jacking points at which forces can be applied are incorporated in these cross stretchers, which means that the lifting beam of a breakdown crane making an 'end-on' lift of a Class 47 has to project over the locomotive body about 10ft to reach it, a fact upon which wry comment has been made by more than one breakdown foreman. Even so, the Class 47 is an easier

fig 3

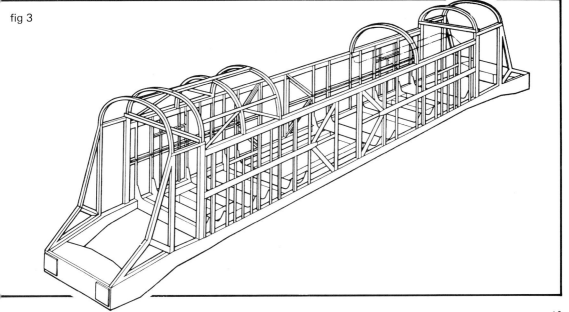

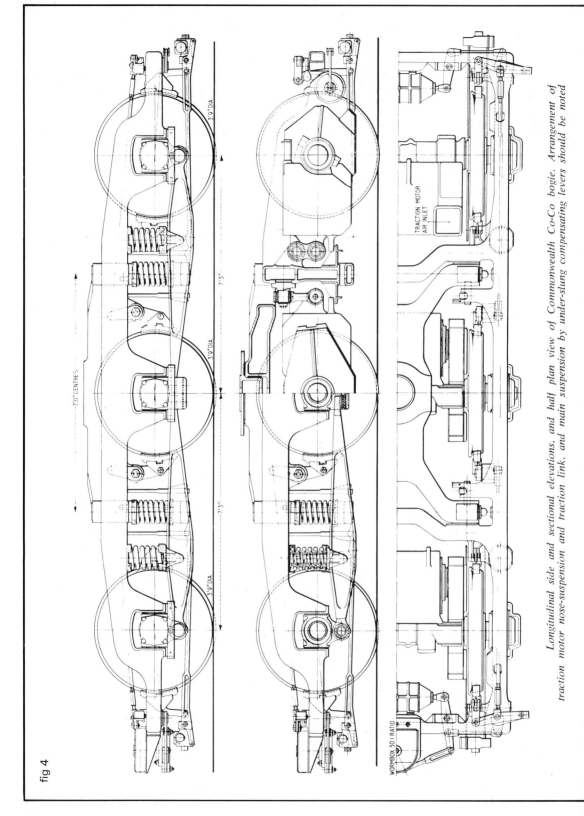

fig 4

7'0"CENTRES

7'3"

7'3"

3'9"DIA

3'9"DIA

3'9"DIA

3'9"DIA

TRACTION MOTOR AIR INLET

WORMBOX 50:1 RATIO

Longitudinal side and sectional elevations, and half plan view of Commonwealth Co-Co bogie. Arrangement of traction motor nose-suspension and traction link, and main suspension by under-slung compensating levers should be noted

Above: Commonwealth bogie complete. / *Brush*

comotive to lift or jack when derailed than a 1Co-Col achine, for which fact the same foremen have been ankful!

The general form of construction of the Commonwealth bogie is shown in Figs 4 and 5 and photo above. The frames are of cast manganese steel to obtain the owest weight consistent with strength. The primary and econdary suspension is by coil springs and anyone who as ridden on these locomotives at their maximum speed f 95mph can confirm the satisfactory riding qualities herent in this design of bogie, which gives a mean ride dex, lateral and vertical, of about 3.5 at 90mph.

The brake gear is remarkable for the ingenious system f bell cranks, beams, hangers and pull rods required in rder to provide clasp brakes on all three bogie axles, ven though only two brake cylinders are fitted to each ogie. The fact that when a bogie is moving at speed its

motion is never completely smooth and straight in either vertical or lateral planes, means that any fittings freely suspended from it, such as a brake block hanger, will develop a lateral swinging motion.

The stretcher rods and pull rods attached to the bottom of the hangers are weighty and because the bogie has to negotiate curves, clearance has to be provided between all moving parts. The inertia of this mass of brake rigging at speed is considerable and leads to wear of connecting pins and all rubbing surfaces. Wear due to this cause was excessive on the earlier Class 47 locomotives and was aggravated by the slack adjusters suspended from the brake hangers. An improvement was effected by stabilising the outer brake hangers through the addition of

5

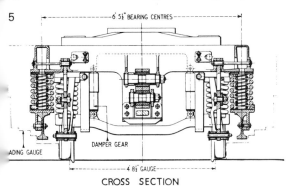

CROSS SECTION

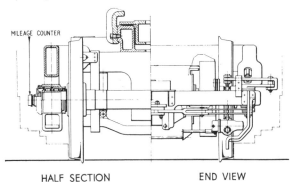

HALF SECTION   END VIEW

retaining brackets, and replacing heavy intermediate stretchers by fabricated bars of box section which are solidly attached to the brake hangers and completely separated from the pull rod pins. The rigidity of the rigging was also improved by increasing the bearing surfaces of connecting pins and reducing clearances. The modified arrangement is shown in Fig 6.

An important part of any locomotive is the driving cab, for here the interface between man and machine is situated. In many earlier designs of diesel locomotive, the designer had failed to realise that the design of many items of equipment and their lay-out is governed by the physiological and anatomical capabilities and limitations of the human being destined to operate them. This fact had been fully appreciated by the Brush design staff by the time that the Class 47 design was being developed. Apart from draughts which entered the cab from some unintended sources in the body floor and lowered the temperature to an unacceptable degree in cold weather, drivers found little cause for complaint.

Early batches of Class 47s were fitted with vacuum train brake equipment. The driver's valve of this system is used to apply the air brake on the locomotive in synchronisation with the vacuum brake on the train, but a driver's self-lapping straight air brake valve is also provided to enable the brake to be applied on the locomotive so that a partially fitted train can be 'gathered together' before the brake is applied on the fitted portion. It is also used when the locomotive is running light.

Subsequently, however, all the existing fleet of 507 Class 47 locomotives have been fitted with air brake apparatus, either as built new or by subsequent modification, to enable them to work air-braked trains. If ever there was proof of universal demand for a relatively high-powered locomotive of great versatility, this was it. The retrospective fitting cost £12,000-£13,000 per locomotive — a sum greatly in excess of that which would have been incurred if the air brake equipment for the train had been incorporated in the locomotives when built. The whole of the fleet was to have been fitted with air brakes before the end of 1976.

It is convenient here to examine the present situation relating to power brakes on BR, although to do justice to the subject a whole volume would be needed. There are three categories into which locomotive-hauled vehicles may be grouped according to their brake characteristics. They are:

1 Vehicles not fitted with power brakes
2 Vehicles with automatic brakes, applied by a reduction in train pipe vacuum
3 Vehicles with automatic air brakes, applied by a reduction in train pipe air pressure.

For a locomotive to be fully versatile, it must be able to stop trains fitted with either air or vacuum brakes or those without continuous brakes. In the last case, the locomotive must have sufficient weight, in addition to brake force. All of the Class 47 fleet are able to work trains in any of these three categories.

The designers of the brake equipment, Davies & Metcalfe, (Westinghouse for Nos 47.401 to 47.420) faced a requirement for the locomotive air brakes and two types of continuous train brakes to be controlled from one brake valve in each cab. As a further complication, on goods trains (whether air-or vacuum-braked) it was stipulated that, following a brake application by the driver, the locomotive brakes must not come fully into use until some 30sec after application of the train brakes, this was to prevent any damaging and dangerous bunching of vehicles behind the locomotive.

Each locomotive carries two air compressors and two vacuum exhausters. Fig 7 shows a schematic layout of the basic system. With an air-braked train, the driver's brake valve (DBV) controls the application of the locomotive brakes by reducing the air train pipe (ATP) pressure from the normal 70lb/sq in to 48lb/sq in for a full service application. This pressure reduction causes the distributor (D) to send an air pressure signal to relay valve (RV), which permits controlled air flows from the main air reservoirs (MR) to the brake cylinders (BC). On the vehicles behind the

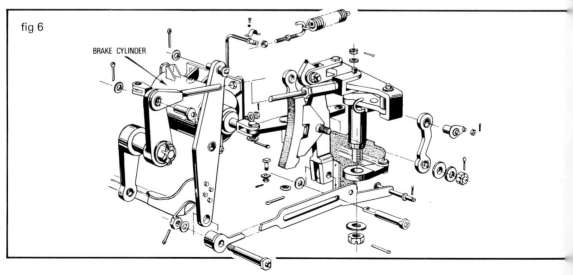

fig 6

BRAKE CYLINDER

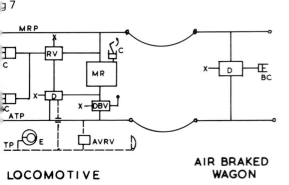

LOCOMOTIVE   **AIR BRAKED WAGON**

RAKE SCHEMATIC (SIMPLIFIED)

locomotive, the brakes are similarly applied by the drop in air train pipe pressure, but here the distributors supply air directly from the auxiliary air reservoirs; which are fed from the locomotive via the main reservoir pipe (MRP) to brake cylinders. The apparent complexity of the system arises because of the need to control brake force accurately throughout the train. This could not be achieved if the air for all vehicle brake cylinders had to pass directly through the driver's brake valve. The locomotive and train air brakes are released quickly by overcharging the air train pipe to 76lb/sq in and allowing it to bleed down slowly to 70lb/sq in. Too fast a bleed down would signal a further light application and dragging brakes. On vacuum-braked trains, the driver's brake valve still controls the pressure in the air train pipe, which of course runs only through the locomotive. However, the level of pressure in the air train pipe dictates, via the air/vacuum relay valve (AVRV), the level of vacuum in the vacuum train pipe (VTP); this controls the vacuum brakes on the train, and, by means of a special diaphragm in the distributor, the locomotive brakes. The train brakes are quickly released by boosting (speeding up) the exhausters.

The locomotive controls include a four-way switch which sets the locomotive to work either an air-braked or vacuum-braked passenger train or, by choking the air train pipe signal to the distributor, on an air-braked or vacuum-braked freight train.

Goods trains without continuous brakes rely for braking on judicious use of the locomotive straight air brake valve, which signals two relay valves to pass air to the locomotive brake cylinders. This valve is sometimes used to gather together a fitted, or partially-fitted, freight train before the train brakes are applied, thus avoiding violent bunching of the vehicles and potential injury to the guard. Both the driver's valves are self-lapping — that is, they set a specified brake force at each handle position, rather than a specified rate of air flow from, or into, the train pipes.

Little mention has been made of the power equipment of the locomotive in this introductory chapter. The prime mover, the diesel engine itself, is the culmination of many years of intensive development work by the Sulzer Company of Winterthur, Switzerland. The generator and traction motors are products of the Brush factory at Loughborough, where 310 of the total of 512 Class 47s were built, the remainder emanating from BR's Crewe Works. The description of these primary machines occupies the succeeding chapter; meanwhile this one is concluded by a table of some relevant particulars of the locomotives.

Leading particulars of Brush 2,750bhp, Co-Co Class 47 Locomotives

Type of engine:	Turbo-charged and charge-cooled Sulzer 12LDA28-C 12-cylinder twin-bank
Nominal engine output:	2,750bhp
Wheel diameter:	3ft 9in
Bogie wheelbase:	14ft 6in
Total wheelbase:	51ft 6in
Overall length:	63ft 6in
Overall height from rail level:	12ft 9$\frac{3}{8}$in (with new tyres)
Minimum clearance to rail:	6in (with new tyres)

TRANSMISSION EQUIPMENT

Main generator, rigidly coupled to engine output shaft, Brush type

Excitation: series, shunt and separate

Continuous ratings:	2,130A 844V 1,152rpm
	1,860A 970V 1,152rpm
1-hour rating:	2,350A 762V 1,152rpm
Continuous ratings:	4,260A 422V 1,152rpm
	3,720A 485V 1,152rpm
1-hour rating:	4,700A 381V 1,152rpm

TRACTION MOTORS

Number: 6, Brush type (connected either 2 × 3 in series parallel or 1 × 6 in parallel)

Description: Nose suspended, series wound, force ventilated with roller suspension bearings and torsionally resilient gear wheels

TRACTION MOTOR RATINGS

	1 hour	Continuous
Locomotive speed, mph	24	27
Engine speed, rpm	800	800
Current, motor	783A	705A
Volts, motor	381V	422V
Output	298kW	298kW
Tractive effort at rail	32,810lb	30,000lb
Tractive effort, maximum	55,000lb	—

MISCELLANEOUS DETAILS

Maximum speed of locomotive:	95mph
Weight in working order:	111 tons 18cwt to
(varies according to different equipment in different batches)	118 tons 14cwt
Minimum curve radius:	4 chains
Fuel tank capacity:	810gal

2 The Sulzer/Brush Power Equipment

Sulzer first entered the locomotive engine field in 1912, when they were partners in a company with Dr Rudolf Diesel called Thermolocomotive which built a 2-B-2 direct-drive 1,000hp locomotive to the order of the Prussian State Railways. This locomotive showed direct drive to be quite unsuited to traction and it did no useful work. The first World War intervened and no further main-line locomotive work was actually undertaken until 1932, when an experimental 2Eo1 locomotive was built to the specifications of Professor Lomonosoff for the USSR, this time with electric transmission. Indeed, Sulzer had been associated almost entirely with electric transmission to the present day, except for a small number (48) of shunting locomotives with hydraulic transmissions.

In the 1930s Sulzer conceived the idea of a range of engines which would all have similar design features and constructional details, though only limited standardisation. They were to cover a power range of 180-1,200hp and it was from this basic idea that the LDA range of engines was evolved and emerged in 1935/6.

An epoch-making design for its time, and capable of development as time went on, the basic elements and proportions of the LDA range served for all new construction up to the mid-1960s. It is doubtful if its originators even envisaged the power increase of 55% per unit of cylinder volume for pressure-charged engines which was gained in 25 years of development based on four cylinder bores, viz 220mm, 250mm, 280mm and 310mm. The range, even in 1936, included 12-cylinder twin-bank designs, since the V configuration in those days was a difficult proposition due to bearing problems.

The first four 12-cylinder twin-bank engines were built in 1936/7. The first two were installed in a 2-Co-2 + 2-Co-2 locomotive ordered by the PLM Railway of France and ran over a million miles before the locomotive was withdrawn. The second two were installed in a 2Do1 + 1Do2 locomotive built by Henschel in 1938 for Rumania and they ran until 1964. All were of the largest cylinder bore, designated 12LDA31 and developed 2,200bhp at 700 crankshaft rpm.

The LDA28 design was one of the first to embody substantial cast-steel transverse members welded into a mild-steel crankcase, which was itself a common structure with the bedplate carrying engine and generator. The cylinder block was of similar construction. Main bearings and fine-adjustment wedges let into the structure, which obviated the need for studded caps, and connecting rod big-end bolts had a toothed locking arrangement.

At the beginning of World War II many LD engines were in service. Most of them were pressure charged and therefore bore the designation LDA (A =abgasturbine — exhaust turbo-supercharger). Sulzer were among the first to realise the potential of the Buchi exhaust turbo-

19

supercharger and developed their own range of turbo-superchargers matched to individual engine requirements.

Little development took place during World War II, but afterwards a reappraisal confirmed the basic principles required for a satisfactory prime mover for traction. These may be summarised as follows:

1 The employment of only the minimum number of cylinders for the required output
2 Relatively low rotational speeds
3 Robust and simple construction
4 Maximum accessibility from all sides
5 Protection of the engine against accidental overloads
6 Conservative mean piston speed.

The first move in the postwar era was to seek an increase in power output. Thus the prewar twin-bank 12LDA31 engine was discontinued for new construction and its place in the production programme was taken over by the smaller-cylindered and less bulky 12LDA28 engine. The 31cm-bore engine could not seriously compete with the more compact engines coming on to the market in the postwar era, especially when the confines of the British loading gauge had to be considered.

That lightweight locomotives employing the LDA28 engine were certainly practical was demonstrated by SLM's construction for the Swiss Federal Raiwlays in 1939 of two Bo-Bo 1,200bhp diesel-electric locomotives which weighed 65 tonnes apiece. The 8LDA28 engine was employed, driving a main dc traction generator and train heating alternator in the same frame and running at 750rpm. These two locomotives (originally numbered 1001 and 1002, later renumbered 18451 and 18452) covered 770,000 and 910,000 miles respectively up to 1976.

In the immediate postwar period, minor improvements were made and the 6LDA28 engines supplied to the CIE had their output increased from 900 to 960bhp at 750rpm. It was the vast improvement in bearing materials toegether with the advances in lubricants and piston cooling which began the significant increases in specific engine output. By 1954 the 6LDA28 engine was developing 1,050bhp at 750rpm, while by 1955 12LDA28 twin-bank engines giving an output of 2,000bhp at 710rpm were in service in SNCF Co-Co bogie locomotives for the Paris Ceinture line.

The announcement that British Railways were contemplating widespread dieselisation led the Sulzer company to review the design again with a view to quantity production, and to consider whether an alternative type, at that time being designed, might be a more acceptable proposition. In the event, it was decided to continue the process of improvement and uprating of the whole LDA range to the point of optimum performance, but in parallel with development of the new range of engines, to be designated LVA24.

By the time the BR pilot dieselisation scheme was announced certain major changes had been made. These included oil-cooled pistons, flash-type tri-metal bearings for crankshaft and connecting rod big-ends, and viscous-type torsional vibration dampers in place of the former pendulum type, and new governors. At the same time a complete investigation into the combustion and thermal performance of the engines was carried out. In consequence, when the BR pilot scheme enquiries were sent out in 1955 the 6 and 12LDA28 engines met the specifications of the projected Type B and Type C locomotives, set respectively at 1,160 and 2,300hp at 750rpm. Thus orders were received for 40 engines of type 6LDA28 and 10 engines of type 12LDA28, the locomotives embodying them to be delivered in 1958 and 1959 respectively. These locomotives are now designated by BR as Class 24 and 44 respectively. The first engines for them were made in Winterthur, Switzerland.

It was from these small beginnings that the present engines which power the fleet of Class 47 locomotives were derived. Although the Class 44 locomotives met the conditions imposed when they were delivered, their power/weight ratio was not satisfactory and this was not rectified in the subsequent Classes 45 and 46. But private industry pointed the way and it took the lead in designing a locomotive capable of taking a single medium-speed engine in the 2,500/3,000hp range, yet remaining within the 19ton axle load limitation; this was the prototype *Lion*.

The principal changes applied to the 12LDA28-A engines as fitted to the BR Class 44 locomotives, before further examples were installed in the BR Class 45 and 46 locomotives, included an increase in the level of super-charging, together with cooling of the supercharge air in order to limit thermal stressing. Other modifications made at a later date included strengthened cylinder heads and more effective lubricating oil filtration. So the B form of the engine was born, with a continuous traction rating of 2,500bhp at 750rpm.

Actually these were not the first engines in Britain to be rated at 2,500bhp. One of the Class 44 locomotives — No D2 as it was then numbered — had its engine fitted with a supercharge-air cooler and was temporarily uprated to 2,500bhp for trial purposes, though the traction motors and gear ratio remained unchanged. While about 9% extra horsepower was available at the wheel tread over much of the operating speed range, however, the power available at the high speed end remained the same — because the additional power could not be absorbed by the electric transmission at speeds in excess of 75mph. As a result of this trial, when the order was given for 127 locomotives of 2,500bhp a slightly different design of traction motor was specified. This was partly to save some weight, but in addition different characteristics were introduced to enable the additional power to be transmitted to the wheels as close to the maximum operating speed of 90mph as possible. So the further order for 56 locomotives — now designated Class 46 — specified the same engine, but Brush

electrical equipment in place of that supplied by Crompton Parkinson in the earlier batches of Class 44 and 45 locomotives.

In 1959 BR was pressing for still more power output, at first to cover the provision of electric train heating, but later as a traffic requirement. It was decided therefore to modify the engine further to enable it to run at a still higher rating. Supercharge air cooling was increased, crankshaft speed was raised to 800rpm and the piston/connecting-rod assembly was strengthened to take care of the higher inertia forces involved. In this form the engine is designated 12LDA28-C and its nominal traction rating is 2,750bhp at 800rpm. One engine was put through the UIC 100hr-type test to ORE Specification 263-OR in July 1962, which it successfully completed in the presence of BR and SNCF inspectors.

By the middle of 1962 the first batch of 20 Class 47 locomotives was under construction at the Brush Company's works in Loughborough and the need for powerful diesel motive power was so urgent that further orders were already in hand. These 20 locomotives were to be the forerunners of the largest class of high-horsepower, general-purpose main-line diesel locomotives on British Railways. Like other Continental engine builders, Sulzer now had to seek manufacturing facilities in the United Kingdom. As the company was already established in the United Kingdom it was decided to sub-contract the engine building to an engineering firm with diesel engine experience rather than to employ a licensee. The firm of Vickers-Armstrong at Barrow was chosen, as it had the necessary facilities to manufacture the type of engine involved, the capacity for bulk production which would be essential to fulfil the requirements of British Railways and other potential customers; together with the back-up of spares to cover the working life of the equipment. The whole programme was managed by the Traction Division of Sulzer Bros (London) Ltd as agents of the parent company in Switzerland and the British company was strengthened to provide the contract, project and technical liaison services required; design and development work were undertaken in Switzerland.

When one considers the scale of BR's dieselisation programme — the magnitude of which has not been matched by any other *single* administration anywhere in the world — it is clear that very little time was available for thorough proving of designs. Inevitably, the work involved in implementing design changes resulted in minor and sometimes major modification work that had to be carried out over quite long periods of time. Moreover, once embarked on a modernisation programme, BR very soon appreciated that dieselisation produced the quickest return on capital. They were anxious to press ahead with the replacement of steam as quickly as possible. Whether this policy was the correct one will doubtless be argued for many years to come. What is clear beyond doubt is that *Lion* would not have appeared as early as 1962 if engine development work, already well advanced by 1960, had not made further substantial progress.

As in the case of the temporarily uprated 12LDA28-A engine of Class 44 locomotive No D2, the 12LDA28-B

engine, this time in locomotive No D57, was up-rated temporarily to 2,750bhp but still at 750rpm. The increased cooling capacity necessary was provided by pressurising the cooling system and running the engine with higher coolant temperature than was then normal.

As a result of this trial and a close examination by the engine designers of the design parameters of the 12LDA28-B engine, the conclusion was reached that only relatively minor modifications would be necessary to enable its output to be increased by 10%. There was a choice between increasing the brake mean effective pressure in the cylinders or increasing the crankshaft rpm. The second alternative was adopted, since connecting-rod bearing pressures would remain substantially the same as for the B engine and the same big-end bearings could be employed. Thus the 12LDA28-C engine was offered to BR at 2,750bhp at 800rpm with the output shaft running at 1,152rpm. As already mentioned, the principal changes were larger intercoolers, strengthened connecting-rod/ piston assemblies and a modified water cooling circuit. In this form the engine was fitted into the first 20 Class 47 locomotives, then Nos D1500-1519 (now Nos 47.401-20).

Particular attention was paid in the design to ensure highly efficient fuel combustion resulting in low fuel consumption. Controlled injection timing gives a good consumption over the full working range, which has even greater significance than the saving of fuel costs which results from it, because by keeping the heat losses to a minimum, the engine is kept clean and maintenance costs are reduced.

The cylinder block is of the wet liner type with a heavy-section top plate and a central welded-in inlet water pipe. A single camshaft on the outside of each cylinder bank is used for the operation of the valve gear and fuel-injection pumps. Three glass fibre inspection panels and one full-length steel cover on each side of the engine give access to fuel pumps and crankcase respectively. When the big-end caps and cylinder heads are removed, the pistons and rods can be drawn upwards through the cylinder bore.

The crankcase is an integral structure made up of a series of transverse members welded to mild-steel fabricated longitudinal plates. A cross member is fitted at each main bearing position and also at the output gear bearing positions. The box-form side girders are extended to provide a mounting for the generator. The bottom is closed by the sump to complete the crank chamber. Large-diameter oil pipes are welded in, forming an

Left: Connecting rod showing toothed locking rings.
/ *Sulzer Bros (UK) Ltd*

integral part of the structure. The transverse members are carried up to cylinder liner level and form the attachment facings for corresponding members in the cylinder block fabrication.

The two crankshafts are of heat-treated alloy steel, fully machined with balance weights bolted and locked in position, and have elliptical crank webs. By using soft metal bearing material, extra hardening of the shaft is not required and thus surface cracking is eliminated. The journals are finish-ground and hollow-bored to reduce weight and eliminate the necessity for diagonally drilled oilways, which otherwise would pass through highly stressed areas of the shaft.

Main bearings are of the tri-metal type, steel-backed and copper lead-lined with a soft permanent running surface. The advantage of the softness of the base metal is thus combined with the strength of copper-lead to give a bearing which has a long life.

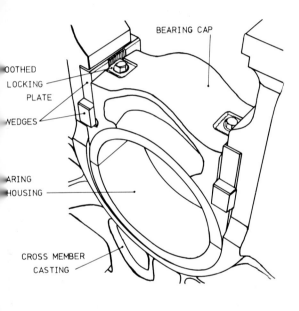

BEARING CAP

TOOTHED LOCKING PLATE

WEDGES

BEARING HOUSING

CROSS MEMBER CASTING

CRANKSHAFT BEARING LOCKING DEVICE

fig 8

The bearing shells are precision-made and are immediately interchangeable without hand fitting or using shims. With the design of bearing construction employed, studded caps, top and bottom are avoided. The lower bearing shell is fully supported underneath by the framing, whilst the top cap is set into the frame and secured by a special wedging arrangement (Fig 8). This fixing is capable of taking its share in the distribution of vertical and transverse loads through the frame structure without studs subject to tension or shear. The wedges are held in position by toothed locking washers which prevent any looseness developing.

A Holset vibration damper is fitted to the free end of each crankshaft. This limits the amplitude of torsional vibrations in such a way that there is no restriction on choice of engine speed over the full working range.

The individual cylinder heads are of alloy cast iron with an open combustion space and porting designed to aero-dynamic standards, thus permitting the use of only one inlet and one exhaust valve per cylinder. This makes for a simple casting. The injector is fitted centrally and provision is made for the fitting of an indicator to measure the peak pressures obtained in the cylinder.

Camshafts are built up from completely solid shafts machined to take the removable cams, which are held in position by circular nuts. The camshaft is housed in white-metal steel-backed bearing shells and the complete shaft can be withdrawn sideways from the engine after removal of the bearing caps. All cams are identical and can be removed individually from the shaft in situ by slackening back one, or at the most, two of the cam securing nuts. The camshaft is gear-driven from the crankshaft.

The valves are operated through push rods and rocker arms and all moving parts including the valve tappets are automatically lubricated. The inlet and exhaust valves are identical.

Connecting rods are of H-section nickel-chrome forged steel, machined all over to reduce weight so as to avoid highly stressed irregularities in the surface of the forging and to obtain accurate balance. The rods are drilled in the longitudinal axis to carry lubricating oil from the big-ends to the small-ends, and for cooling purposes, to the piston. The big-end bearings are similar to the main bearings, being of the tri-metal type, but the caps are located by bolts whose nuts are locked by a special toothed device avoiding the use of split pins (see photo p22). The small end bearings have a steel back with a layer of copper-lead.

The two-piece pistons are of aluminium alloy, machined inside and out. Lubricating oil from the engine system, is fed from the fully floating gudgeon pin through channels immediately behind the piston ring grooves and afterwards discharged vertically downwards into the crankcase. The ring grooves are thus kept cool, and the whole piston ring mechanism maintained free from sticking and excessive wear. There are three pressure rings and one scraper ring above the gudgeon pin and one scraper ring below. The top pressure ring is chromium-plated and initially is copper-plated also to assist running-in.

The governor is of Sulzer design and is of the servo-operated, continuous speed-torque control type. As its oil feed is taken from the engine system is fails to safety on loss of lubricating oil pressure. One locomotive No D1880 (new No 47.361) was fitted experimentally with a Sulzer electronic governor with provision for tractive effort control; this has since been removed in the interests of standardisation.

To prevent the injection of excessive fuel during starting or when accelerating the engine, the governor includes a pressure charging protection device, which limits the fuel injected at any time to below the theoretical smoke limit permitted in the exhaust. Thus the amount of fuel injected is always matched to the amount of air available for combustion, which is especially important until the exhaust turbine has reached its full speed at any controller position.

Below: The prestige Pullman service 'The Master Cutler' provided one of the few opportunities for a Brush Type 4 to carry a headboard. In this interesting view of the up train at Belle Isle, note the unusual placing of the shedcode plate below the headcode panel, and also the earlier type radiator panel on the roof. / *Eric Treacy*

An engine overspeed device is provided. This is the spring-loaded flyweight type and shuts down the engine by actuating the linkage to the fuel regulating shaft if the maximum permitted crankshaft rpm are exceeded.

Fuel is fed to the fuel pumps under slight pressure by a transfer pump. It is part of the combined fuel, lubricating oil priming and water pump set, which is driven by a traction-type electric motor. Pressurising the feed to the injection pumps ensures even flow without cavitation on the low pressure side under all conditions of acceleration and deceleration of the engine and the locomotive.

Filtration of the fuel is effected by a full-flow strainer and paper cartridge filter, which ensures absolute cleanliness of the fuel passed to the injection pumps.

The fuel injection equipment incorporates several Sulzer features, such as injection timing control, which is achieved by having a double helix pump plunger that advances the point of injection with increasing engine speed. By this means the injection timing is the optimum at all engine speeds and power outputs, with uniform combustion and economical running under varying conditions.

Fuel is delivered from the fuel injection pump through piping to a point on the outside of the cylinder head and then to the injector through a drilled stud. This stud screws into the injector body with a normal high pressure joint but also incorporates a low pressure joint. Any leakage from these joints is taken by a passage into the leak-off pipe and away to waste and prevents any possibility of contamination of the lubricating oil by fuel oil.

Any fuel injection pump can be easily disconnected from and re-connected to the control shaft whilst the engine is running by means of a small spring-loaded lever. This is invaluable for test purposes and for isolating a defective pump or injector by the driver in service in an emergency.

Lubricating oil is drawn from the sump through a coarse filter by the engine-driven pump and passed to the heat exchanger which is mounted on the engine. The engine cooling water is circulated through the heat exchanger to warm the oil on starting and to keep it at its optimum temperature thereafter. Good lubrication conditions are thus obtained quickly after starting and maintained by the thermostatic control of the engine cooling water. By mounting the heat exchanger on the engine no major oil pipes leave the engine.

The system is thoroughly primed before engine starting by a lubricating oil priming pump, which is part of the combined set referred to earlier. The pump set continues to run for a short time after engine shut down to provide an even temperature gradient as the system cools down.

Particular attention is paid to oil filtration. After leaving the heat exchanger the oil passes to a combined full flow coarse and bypass fine filter, the latter separating particles down to one micron size and maintaining the oil in good condition for long periods.

Safety devices are provided which cause the engine to shut down automatically in the event of the following conditions arising: lubricating oil pressure too low; engine overspeed; cooling water pressure too low. In the event of excessive cooling water temperature a warning lamp is illuminated. Since the oil is cooled in the heat exchanger, excessive lubricating oil temperature will not occur without excessive water temperature.

Other technical data relating to the 12LDA28-C engines as originally fitted is shown in the table below.

The 12LDA28-C Sulzer Engine as built: general data

Continuous rating:	2,750bhp (UIC rating)	Method of starting:	Motoring main generator
One hour test bed rating:	3,025bhp at 800rpm	Breakaway torque (at 32°F):	6,680lb ft
Continuous rated speed:	800rpm	Min firing speed:	130rpm
No of cylinders:	12, twin-bank, in line with crankshafts geared to common output shaft	Torque at min firing speed (at 32°F):	2,680lb ft
Bore and stroke of cylinders:	280mm bore, 360mm stroke	Description of cooling system:	Forced water circulation system for engine water jacket, lubricating oil heat exchanger and charge air intercooling
Type of combustion chamber:	Open — direct injection		
Mean piston speed at rated rpm:	1,888ft/min		
Brake mean effective pressure at cont rating:	168lb/sq in	Cooling data (at continuous rating):	
Max cylinder pressure at continuous rating:	1,422lb/sq in	Quantity of heat to be dissipated:	4,560,000BTUs/hr
Compression pressure at idling speed and no load:	520lb/sq in	Water flow:	19,800gal/hr
Class of fuel recommended:	BS2869 Class A or B	Normal water temp:	178°F
Specific fuel consumption (fuel 18,400 BTUs) at continuous rating:	0.365lb/bhp/hr, tolerance +5%	Type of lubricating oil recommended:	Heavy duty SAE30 or 40 to Specification DEF 2101B
Fuel consumption at minimum idling speed:	30lb/hr	Average lubricating oil consumption in service:	1/300 of fuel consumption
Min idling speed:	325rpm	Lubricating oil pressure:	60lb/sq in (at continuous rating)
Max governed speed at no load:	830rpm	Lubricating oil temperature:	185°F (at continuous rating)
Ratio output shaft speed to crankshaft speed:	1.44 : 1	Approx air consumption at continuous rating:	7,650cu ft/min
Direction of rotation (drive end):	Clockwise	Max exhaust back pressure:	20in Water Gauge

3 Engine Building gets under way

As the BR dieselisation programme gathered momentum, locomotive power equipment manufacturers had to make use of all available production resources within the United Kingdom if locomotives were to be produced in the most economical manner. In effect there were nine separate locomotive builders (including four British Rail workshops at Derby, Crewe, Darlington and Swindon), of which six were installing Sulzer engines, and engine production at the Vickers works at Barrow-in-Furness on a large scale was essential.

In anticipation of the demand, the Vickers management set aside a complete section of their works at Barrow for the assembly of Sulzer engines, while component manufacture was organised to feed the assembly shop at the appropriate rate. At one stage the working rate enabled completion of one engine, fully tested, per working day and this peak of production was reached in 1963-64. Demand was such that six and eight-cylinder in-line engines were built simultaneously with the 12-cylinder twin-bank engines.

Sulzer engine design policy ensures that engines are suitable for production anywhere in the world with general purpose machinery only. But the BR programme was on a scale that justified special jigs and tools. In particular, the crankcase of the 12-cylinder, twin-bank engines — equivalent to two six-cylinder engines joined longitudinally — could be machined to the required tolerances in one setting if a special line-boring rig was employed which could deal with the two crankshaft bearing housings and that of the output shaft in one operation, thus ensuring accurate alignment of all three. The machine is shown in the photograph on p28. An outstanding feature of the whole engine building operation was the elimination, wherever practical, of hand fitting both in the intermediate operations and on final assembly and this involved accurate machining of all components.

The principal features of the production process were fabrication of the main components, eg cylinder blocks, crankcases, both employing not only cast steel cross members but also pre-formed and welded platework. Extensive pre-machining, bending and forming of all platework in bulk quantities required the use of burning

Left: Another Pullman service to which the class was assigned was the 'Bournemouth Belle', although this lasted only until electrification was completed. Here, with its two-tone livery obliterated by dirt D1686 heads the train for the first time on 1 May 1967, diverted via Alton due to engineering work. / *C. Small*

Above: Crankcase line boring machines.

and bending machines on a wide scale. Special jigs and manipulators were employed to produce accurate fabrications with the minimum of handling between operations. The whole fabrication department was laid out on a flow-line basis to facilitate production and accurate machining to fine limits so as to eliminate hand fitting and to ensure maximum interchangeability. Some of the most interesting operations are outlined below.

The special-purpose machine for machining crankshaft housing bores was built by Vickers and employed three Brooke individual driving heads. A design tolerance of a maximum deviation in any direction of 0.0006in was required and this figure was maintained by frequent checks of the boring rig rather than the finished work. The complete machine has now been purchased by British Rail Engineering Ltd and installed in Crewe Works, where the half-life reconditioning of the engines is now in progress.

Cylinder blocks were machined and ground three at once on an 18ft vertical boring machine to ensure an accuracy of 0.0005in. Pistons were completely machined using tracing techniques. As the ring-carrier is a separate part, retained by interference fit, a diamond tool is used to finish the mating faces of both the piston and ring carriers. A special plant heats the ring carrier to 185°C and the piston body is frozen to −60°C to permit assembly with the predetermined interference of 0.015-0.018in. After the whole piston has attained normal workshop temperature, a hydraulic pressure test at 175lb/sq in is given using paraffin. Connecting rods are forged from a nickel chrome molybdenum steel and machined all over. A longitudinal hole passes through the centre from large to small end and is approximately ⅝in dia and 21in long. To ensure accuracy, the drilling head employed withdraws and returns the drill at frequent intervals to clear the swarf.

To couple the two crankshafts together and to the output shaft, precision ground synchronising gears are employed. These gears and other driving gears in the engine are ground in a special shop under controlled temperature and humidity conditions, temperature being maintained at 68°F (20°C) and humidity at 60%. Full interchangeability of gears is guaranteed, and is also ensured by the accuracy of the crankcase boring method described above.

Sub-assemblies were employed to facilitate erection and where possible pre-set and tested assemblies of components, such as governors, fuel pumps, turbo pressure-chargers wre provided to avoid setting-up time. Final erection took place in three main stages. The first stage included the fitting and dowelling of all end covers, driving components and ancillary components, e.g. lubricating oil pumps, filters etc.

The second stage was completely to dismantle the running components and clean the crankcase and cylinder block in a cleansing tank containing fuel oil and paraffin, which was pumped under pressure through an internal piping to ensure complete removal of all machining swarf.

The third stage of final assembly was carried out in completely clean conditions. Any engine not being worked upon for any reason was protected by strong polyurethane sheeting. Each engine was given full running tests to the requirements of British Standard and BR specifications. A testing bay was built to accommodate three six-cylinder and three eight-cylinder or four 12-cylinder engines on testing beds and electrical equipment was arranged so that six engines could be run simultaneously.

The running tests, designed to meet the requirements of the manufacturer and the customer, consisted of the following schedule:

Engine run at full load for four hours
Engine run at 75% full load for one hour
Engine run at 50% full load for one half hour
Engine run at 25% full load for one half hour
Engine run at 10% overload for one half hour

Governors and other components were checked and at the conclusion of the test programme, each engine was opened up for examination of selected bearings and pistons. The last operation was to paint the engine before despatch to the appropriate builder's works for installation in the locomotive.

The building facilities created at Vickers' Barrow works were to prove invaluable when a crash modification programme had to be mounted, of which more later.

Below: The later-type Serck radiator shutters are clearly visible in this view of D1921 on a Waterloo-Eastleigh crew training run in 1966 when members of the class took over a few of the Bournemouth line workings from ailing steam power, shortly before the commencement of electric services. / *John H. Bird*

4 Development of the Design

With most well-established designs of machinery, development leads to changes, some quite fundamental. But when development is also accompanied by heavy production pressure, proving-time tends to be restricted and the technical/commercial considerations force designers to take what, in retrospect, seem to be short cuts. The 12LDA28 engine was developed in this way, to its detriment at the time.

The reasons behind the decision to increase crankshaft speed from 750 to 800rpm and the changes made to strengthen certain moving parts have already been mentioned. At the time the Sulzer research facilities were fully committed in connection with further development, and so the design of the structural components of the 12LDA28 engine was reviewed in the light of experience then to hand from engines already in service; such improvements as this showed necessary were incorporated. For example, the two main side members of the engine crankcase which are welded box sections were stiffened by closing the box at the generator end; and the sheet steel sump, formerly a pressing, was redesigned as an integral part of the crankcase structure, a feature which had later repercussions.

Thanks to the liaison between the Swiss design engineers, the manufacturing company and the customer, there was a ready and quick exchange of information and it was this liaison which enabled the construction techniques already described to be established.

It should be remembered that Vickers were building the engines as sub-contractors to Sulzer and the latter were responsible to BR for all aspects of the building programme, together with the subsequent feed-back of service experience.

The first batch of 20 12LDA28C engines differ from the remainder in that the crankcases have extended side arms to support the large dc three-generator group used on the first 20 Class 47 locomotives. There were detailed departures from the LDA28B engines, notably in the exhaust and cooling water pipe systems, some not perpetuated beyond the first 20 engines. Many detailed improvements were incorporated as the complete programme progressed both to ease production and to improve reliability in service.

'Teething' troubles are also associated with new designs and, unless a very protracted development period is possible, must be dealt with quickly, especially when a long series is in production or a great deal of retrospective modification work is involved. Sometimes 'teething' persists and then one is faced with a fundamental problem, not always easy to define or to solve. The engine structure problems which received such widespread publicity at the end of 1966 are a case in point, because what at first appeared to be manufacturing difficulties soon assumed the proportions of a full epidemic. The special measures

Left: The livery style finally adopted for the class differed from the XP64 style in having yellow ends and in the placing of the double-arrow symbol. 47.476 heads the 06.35 Penzance-Paddington, near the end of its journey, at Southall on 20 March 1976. / *B. Morrison*

taken by both Sulzer and BR were first to alleviate the problem and later to apply more permanent improvements. A special operation was mounted, later to be known as 'The Rebalancing Programme' and the events leading to this series of modifications, which were applied to the 12LDA28B engine also, are now described.

It will be recalled that the engine is based on a fabricated structure employing cast steel cross members and steel plate welded together. It is also a fact that a twin-crankshaft engine poses special balancing problems, as space considerations dictate that the two crankshafts must be as close together as the running clearances between them and the related parts permit. This latter point determines the relatively small range of angular displacement between the two shafts. Balance weights must be provided to deal with a proportion of the reciprocating masses and the rotating masses, their size and distribution being dictated by considerations of space and other factors. The whole subject of balancing is in the end a compromise, for which there may be more than one solution.

At the time the Class 47 locomotives were ordered some experience had been gained with the 12LDA28B engines and as already mentioned, in order to prove certain design changes one engine was temporarily up-rated to 2,750bhp at 750rpm in Class 45 locomotive No D57. One of the early 12LDA28C engines was also put through the UIC 100hr type-test but this time running at 800rpm. Neither test indicated any cause for anxiety, so that when the first 20 locomotives of Class 47 were already in service, pressure from the operating department was such that further orders for identical engines were given. It was not until some time later that fatigue cracks were discovered at certain locations in the crankcases of 12LDA28B engines, specifically in the welds which joined the cast steel cross members, or in the side walls and horizontal gusset plates between them (Fig 9). Cracks in the horizontal welds between the cylinder block top and side walls were diagnosed as a welding problem and rectified; later cracks which appeared were probably the result of corrosion from using untreated cooling water (Fig 10).

fig 9

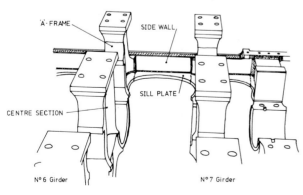

MODIFIED CRANKCASE · PRODUCTION VERSION

fig 10

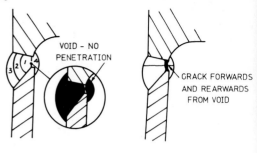

VOID – NO PENETRATION

CRACK FORWARDS AND REARWARDS FROM VOID

ORIGINAL METHOD

Run 4 could be displaced up or down
A few 12 LDA 28 C engines only - early build

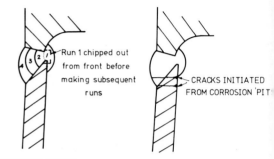

Run 1 chipped out from front before making subsequent runs

CRACKS INITIATED FROM CORROSION 'PIT'

IMPROVED METHOD

Discovery of some sub-standard welding associated with the crankcase cross girders clouded the issue for a while, until cracks at certain positions appeared in the steel castings themselves (Figs 11 & 12). Examination of several crankcases indicated crack initiation from a sharp corner which produced a stress concentration. A modification was advised for those engines already in service, which consisted of removing a portion of the gusset plate containing the sharp change of shape (see Fig 11). The modification was applied retrospectively to all the 12LDA28B engines and 184 crankcases of the 12LDA28C type which were already in service or had been fabricated for engines then being constructed. Concurrently all new construction was altered to a gusset plate having a better profile and greater attention was given to welding methods and inspection. The modifications referred to above were carried out in BR depots and workshops and altogether 101, Class 47 locomotives were modified in service on a special programme.

While the immediate danger appeared to be over, there was concern about the cracks, which did not conform to the general pattern and appeared only on the girder carrying the thrust bearings, which was outside the scope of the modification (Fig 12). Clearly the loading on the girder in question was different as crankshaft end thrust was involved. It took some time to establish the cause of failure, which was finally tracked down to resonance. Resonance may be described as the condition which exists when the natural frequency of vibration of part of a machine has imposed upon it a pulsating torque, such as that resulting from the action of the rapidly expanding

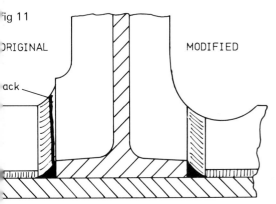

fig 11

ORIGINAL   MODIFIED

ack

N°4 Cross Member Casting

TYPICAL CRACK AND MODIFICATION

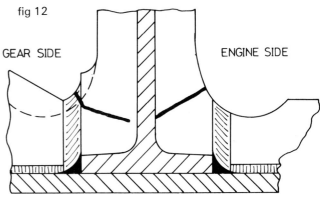

fig 12

GEAR SIDE   ENGINE SIDE

N°7 Cross Member Casting

TYPICAL CRACKS   UNAFFECTED BY
MODIFICATION

gases behind a piston in a cylinder. The frequency of the pulsating torque may increase up to the point where the applied frequency equals the natural frequency, a condition which may result in some parts of the machine becoming very highly stressed. In the case of an internal combustion engine these high stresses occur at certain speeds of revolution of the crankshaft in association with certain piston loadings.

Having established the cause, the remedy took time to find owing to the apparent difficulty of cushioning the forces involved. A quite simple method was applied eventually and involved increasing the longitudinal float of the crankshaft in its bearings. The clue to this solution came from the BR Research Department following a comprehensive series of tests carried out on the line with locomotive No D1733 (47.141). It was noted in the course of these tests that if the clearance was increased sufficently there was only intermittent contact between the crankshaft and the cross member through the bearing thrust face, and resonance of the girder disappeared.

The cracks described above did not give rise to service failures and could be repaired in BR workshops, though not without some loss of revenue due to increased repair cost and additional time on works. It was not until later in 1965 and early 1966 that availability began to suffer when two further specific types of structural failure became apparent. These were respectively, cracks in the sides of the lubricating oil sump and cracks in the internal cooling water feed pipe, the latter being an integral part of the cylinder block. Both fractures resulted in either loss or contamination of lubricating oil. Fortunately both types of failure could be detected before locomotives became casualties, but disruption to train services resulted from the necessity to withdraw the locomotive from traffic working. Unscheduled works attention was necessary and in many cases either complete engines or the major components involved had to be returned to Barrow or repaired in BR workshops.

Viewed in the light of the structural failures then seriously affecting the Mirrlees engines in the Brush Type 2 locomotives, the BR Board not unnaturally expressed grave doubts about the security of their main-line

services. The Chairman of BRB called a meeting with the Chairmen of the companies involved, who assured him that a solution could and would be found and applied quickly. Within four months modifications had been proposed to and agreed with the BR Chief Mechanical & Electrical Engineer, and a major modification programme commenced in April 1966.

Before discussing the programme in detail it is appropriate to pin-point the principal areas of trouble. Mention was made previously of balancing. In a twin-bank engine, rotational out-of-balance forces from the two crankshafts are an important factor in the stressing of the structure. Fatigue in metal structures occurs after an accumulation of a number of harmful cycles — that is, the repeated subjection of parts to harmful alternating stresses. The rate of accumulation is dependent upon the actual method of use of the engine — that is, how near it is run to its maximum output and for how long. To be specific, in the 12LDA28C engine operating at 800rpm, it was found in certain areas that the normally accepted levels of stress were being exceeded and that failure in a comparatively short time was inevitable. These areas have already been mentioned, but in defence of the designers, it should be said that a number of factors led to the conditions ultimately reached; not the least of these was the pressure to keep down engine weight, which led to the use of minimum casting and plate wall thicknesses etc, wherever possible to the minimum dimensions then considered practicable.

Having decided what needed to be done, it was first necessary to ensure that no more harmful stresses were accummulaed than could be avoided. Thus the first action was to reduce the crankshaft revolutions on all engines to 750rpm by a minor governor modification. The result was a reduction in normal engine output of about 6%. Although originally intended as a temporary measure, this has now become a permanent feature to which reference will be made later. The immediate effect was a reduction in the maximum stress in the critical areas by around 10%, although these were still higher than was deemed desirable.

Meanwhile BR had decided to apply certain criteria to

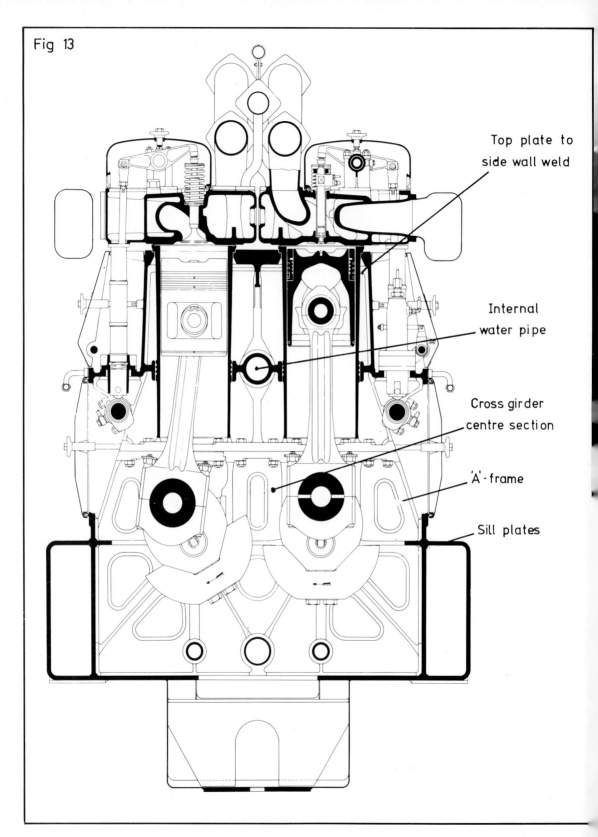

Fig 13

Top plate to side wall weld

Internal water pipe

Cross girder centre section

'A'-frame

Sill plates

he critical areas and now laid down limits of maximum stress which were not to be exceeded. From the requirements it was clear that further measures were necessary if satisfactory operation was to be guaranteed and all stress points were to be within the levels required. As a long-term programme it was necessary to alter the rotational balance. In order to achieve the targets laid down the number of balance weights on both crankshafts was doubled and the angle between the two shafts was increased to the maximum which could be accommodated. The diagram (Fig 13) shows five critical areas. In one case, that of the oil sump, it was necessary to modify the design, which necessitated cutting out and rewelding a complete section. To carry out the modifications it was necessary to strip the engines to fit the crankshafts with the additional balance weights so that Main Works attention again was necessitated.

The organisation set up to make the necessary modifications as quickly as possible is described in the next chapter.

Below: Before the introduction of the 1968 renumbering, the 'D' prefixes were abandoned. Here the 11.10 to St Pancras is about to leave Sheffield behind 1704. Tinted windows were a feature of the Class 47s, but this locomotive appears to have rather more 'tinting' than usual! / *J. H. Cooper-Smith*

5 Mounting the Test and Rebalancing Programme

Before embarking upon a full-scale modification programme to the large fleet of locomotives now in service, it was first necessary to carry out track tests to establish if the engine was subjected to any conditions on the track which could not be reproduced on the Works' test beds.

It had been shown early in 1965 that the failures occurring on the No 7 girder were caused by bending of the girder as a result of longitudinal forces (in line with the crankshafts), and that the resulting stress in the girder was high enough to crack the steel casting. Since both crankshafts drove the generator through gearing there was no longitudinal damping effect from the armature, so that other means had to be sought to cushion the vibrations. Various types of bearing were tried, some employing oil-cushioning of the crankshaft longitudinal movement, some with increased axial clearance intended to 'de-couple' the forces produced by the two shafts.

Locomotive No 1821 (now No 47.340) was used for a series of tests at various times between July and December 1965, either jointly between BR and Sulzer or by BR Research Department alone. The most important factor which emerged was that by increasing the crank shaft end float from 0.2mm to 1.2mm, the rate of build-up of damaging cycles was reduced to $\frac{1}{5}$th at worst to $\frac{1}{90}$th at best.

Over the same period, Sulzer engineers were examining the other critical areas. By the late autumn of 1965 they had crystallised their ideas and had put proposals to BR. The principle of a crash modification programme was accepted in December 1965 by the then Chairman of BR, who was particularly concerned lest availability of the Class 47 fleet should deteriorate further below the 77% figure then obtaining. It was proposed and accepted that a special modification programme should be mounted by Sulzer using facilities which could be made available at Vickers' Barrow Works, provided that 17 spare engines could be used as a float so as to limit locomotive turn-round time to one week.

However, before the crash programme could be implemented, it was considered prudent to do two things. Firstly, to limit the damage to engines already in traffic, the crankshaft speed should be reduced from 800 to 750rpm and the crankshaft end float increased to 1.2mm.

Right: 1642 rolls very gently through the vast lake created by a downpour at Newbury on 11 June 1971. / *E. C. Paine Ltd*

Above: Lifting engine by Barrow Goliath crane. / *Vickers Ltd*

Secondly, a fully modified engine should be checked under service conditions to establish the efficacy beyond doubt of the modifications to be made to such a large number of engines.

Arrangements were made to supply and fit new crankshaft thrust bearings as quickly as they could be obtained. The governor characteristics were modified by exchanging one of the springs in the speed setting section to limit the power reduction to around 2,600bhp at 750rpm; it would have come down to about 2,470bhp if the speed only had been reduced.

For verification of these modifications locomotive No 1773 (now No 47.178) was again selected for running tests before and after, which were conducted by the Locomotive Testing Section with the BR Mobile Testing Unit on behalf of the BR Research Dept, with Sulzer involvement. Preliminary tests were carried out between Stratford and Norwich on 3/4 January 1966 and the locomotive was then sent to Barrow for the engine to be modified. As no special lifting facilities then existed, the engine was removed from the locomotive by one of the shipyard Goliath cranes on 9 February 1966 and the accompanying photograph shows the operation in progress.

After comprehensive tests of the fully modified engine BR pronounced themselves satisfied that the measures promised the previous December had indeed produced the expected improvement in engine structure stressing. The chart (Fig 14) shows the percentage reduction in stress levels due to the various measures taken, singly and in combination.

By March 1966 planning for the rebalancing of the entire fleet of 12LDA28 engines, some 727 in all including spares, had advanced to the stage where proposals were put to the BR Board which indicated that the fleet of 526 12LDA28-C engines could be modified by the end of September 1967 and the 201, 12LDA28A & B engines by mid 1968, if some loss of availability could be tolerated by withdrawing eight locomotives from traffic

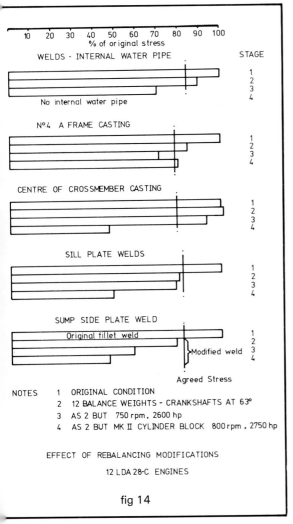

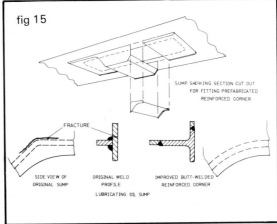

fig 15

SUMP SHOWING SECTION CUT OUT
FOR FITTING PREFABRICATED
REINFORCED CORNER

FRACTURE

SIDE VIEW OF
ORIGINAL SUMP

ORIGINAL WELD
PROFILE

IMPROVED BUTT-WELDED
REINFORCED CORNER

LUBRICATING OIL SUMP

fig 14 (left column diagram)

% of original stress
10 20 30 40 50 60 70 80 90 100

WELDS - INTERNAL WATER PIPE   STAGE
1
2
3
4
No internal water pipe

Nº4 A FRAME CASTING
1
2
3
4

CENTRE OF CROSSMEMBER CASTING
1
2
3
4

SILL PLATE WELDS
1
2
3
4

SUMP SIDE PLATE WELD
Original fillet weld   1
2
Modified weld   3
4
Agreed Stress

NOTES   1   ORIGINAL CONDITION
2   12 BALANCE WEIGHTS - CRANKSHAFTS AT 63°
3   AS 2 BUT 750 rpm, 2600 hp
4   AS 2 BUT MK II CYLINDER BLOCK 800 rpm, 2750 hp

EFFECT OF REBALANCING MODIFICATIONS

12 LDA 28-C ENGINES

fig 14

sets per month and were also fitted in works and depots. The displaced bearings which had further life expectancy were re-used in six and eight cylinder engines as required. These two measures were to be temporary expedients, the latter in particular was to remain only until a more sophisticated arrangement could be introduced. In the event both became permanent and for entirely different reasons.

The two most important reasons for introducing a crash modification programme were that additional balance weights had to be fitted to both crankshafts (and one shaft rotated with respect to the other) and the lubricating oil sump had to be strengthened by introducing a new section right across as shown in the sketch (Fig 15). A rolled section was used to take a weld away from the position of highest stress and a welding technique adopted to enable all operations to be completed externally. These two items alone meant that the crash programme would have to be carried out where full workshop facilities were available and as the Vickers production programme was by then running down, the facilities and men were readily available there.

Although Vickers had built many hundreds of diesel engines in their time and had rail access, they did not have the facilities for handling large main line locomotives. They did, however, have a disused building within their Works area which had formerly been used for the maintenance work on steam locomotives used in and around the works and docks. Although no cranage facilities were installed, the area was large enough to provide track facilities and with a minimum amount of demolition of the existing locomotive shed, buildings could be provided to house a 40 ton hoist for the specific task of changing the power units of the 300, Class 47 locomotives it was intended to modify. The area was close to the general engineering shops where the engine modifications were to be carried out. Weather, as usual, played its part in delaying work on the site, and part of the track bed was flooded during the second part of March 1966 so that track could not be installed until the latter part of March. In spite of work proceeding whenever possible, the track and connections to the BR system were not ready in time to receive on 1 April 1966,

for the duration of the crash programme. Availability was then running at about 77% so that another eight locomotives out of traffic would reduce the figure to 75%, against which had to be balanced the gradual improvement expected as the programme progressed, estimated to be the equivalent of lifting the figure to 81% overall in about 18 months from the commencement of the programme.

The first part of the programme, that of reducing engine speed and output by 50rpm and 6% respectively, commenced in the latter part of February 1966. On its own, speed reduction reduced the stress in the engine sump by 11%. Governor springs were changed at all BR works and depots and all engines had been altered by the end of April 1966. Secondly, thanks to the observation made by BR Research Department ie that increasing the crankshaft thrust bearing clearance by 1.0mm to 1.2mm reduced the build-up of damaging cycles on the No 7 girder so remarkably, steps were taken to fit bearings with the larger clearance as soon as they could be made available. Bearings were delivered at the rate of 25 engine

the first locomotive which had to be handled in a manner similar to No 1773. Nevertheless the engine change was completed inside one week and it left Barrow with the first spare engine, fully modified, on Maunday Thursday, April 1966. The accompanying photograph shows the conditions at the site in February and March 1966.

At the date earmarked for the commencement of the programme, there were more new engines to be delivered including 17 spares for BR Crewe Works. As will be seen from the chart (Fig 16), it was intended to build up the rate of intake and release to deal with one locomotive per day (one locomotive in — one other locomotive out). Examination of the work content in the modifications showed that 18 working days were needed from the time an engine was removed from a locomotive to its installation in another locomotive body. Theoretically the engine from locomotive No 21, say, would go into locomotive No 38, or put another way, there were 17 engines (38-21) being worked upon at any one time. BR's permission to delay delivery of their 17 new spare engines was sought and obtained and as a result locomotives Nos 100-1111 were put into service with second-hand engines in order that the required new engines could be fed into the rebalancing programme at the appropriate times.

Six extra balance weights had to be fitted to each crankshaft which involved machining both crankshafts and balance weights as well as the provision of bolts. In addition to the float of engines a further float of crankshafts had to be provided — not only to cover the Barrow programme, but also the requirements of Crewe and later of the Derby Works. For the sump, pre-fabricated sections were provided and were available for the welders after removal of the old section.

In order to keep the work content as low as possible, an engine dismantling procedure was adopted which enabled the cylinder block and crankcase to be separated without, for example, removing cylinder heads and pistons. The crankcase could then be cleaned and modified, crankshafts exchanged and made ready for re-assembly in 14 shifts, double-shift working being the order of the day. Any extraneous work not directly involved with the modification was specifically excluded and the same procedure was enforced on the engine change and locomotive turnround. In cases where other defects were found, work was only authorised if it could be completed without delay to the programmed turnround; any other jobs were noted by BR inspectors and handled by the owning depot.

As the chart shows it was intended to build up to a maximum rate of 25 locomotives per month by November 1966 and to continue at 21-25 locomotives per month to July 1967. Due to a number of factors — the delay in completion of the engine change facilities being one, and difficulty in obtaining sufficient crankshafts another — the start was slower, although a throughput of 25 locomotives was achieved in November 1966, followed by 27 in December 1966 in spite of the Christmas holiday.

Apart from the Barrow programme, similar work was

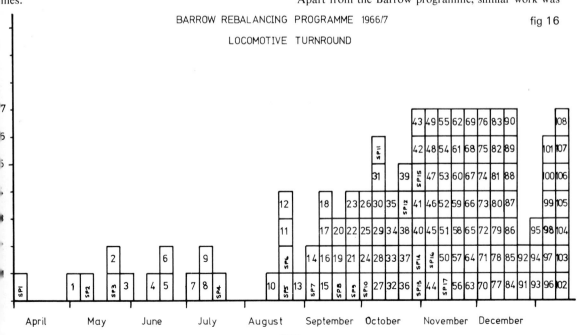

BARROW REBALANCING PROGRAMME 1966/7   fig 16

LOCOMOTIVE TURNROUND

1966

being carried out by BR workshops at Crewe (and at Derby on the 12LDA28-B engines) during and in addition to normal engine overhauls. The rate of modification was determined to some extent by factors outside BR's control and governed by the supply of crankshafts for which Barrow had priority. One principle governing the selection of locomotives to go to Barrow was that the newest, or most recently overhauled should go first since they would then have two years or more to run in traffic before being due for overhaul in one of the main works. This was to avoid a modified locomotive being stopped within a few weeks of engine change. Liaison was such that only very rarely did the wrong locomotive arrive at Barrow, and when one considers there were 500 from which to choose spread over five Regions, that was a good record.

What the Modifications Achieved

The immediate concern in the latter part of 1965 was to prevent a further deterioration in availability and it must be stressed that the engine was by no means the only factor depressing the availability, then running at around 77.5%. It was the sharp drop from 82.5% in June 1965 to 77.5% in August of that year, coupled with a higher than usual incidence of engine defects, which really precipitated the demand for action in view of the relatively low age at which structural defects were occurring, thus putting a heavy overload on BR workshops.

Above: Safety considerations required speedy application of the all-yellow ends and the slow process of repainting the larger classe in rail blue meant that many locomotives remained in green livery after the cab ends were repainted. D1110 was one of the last to be built and remained in green livery until 1974 by which time it had also received its new number, 47.527, in which condition it is seen heading the 09.00 Aberdeen-Kings Cross near Ferryhill. / *B. Morrison*

Right: In the late 1960s the Class 47s began to replace WR diesel-hydraulics on Inter-City expresses. In this 1968 scene an unidentified Class 47 thunders through Reading's centre road as 'Western' Class diesel-hydraulic D1071 waits for the road on a down express. / *A. Wild*

Mention has already been made of the five specifi areas of trouble and how an agreed target stress level ha been assigned to each area, and mention has also bee made of the two stop-gap remedies, ie reducing engin rpm and increasing thrust bearing clearance. The first ha an immediate effect in reducing the rate at which sump were failing and was of immediate benefit to reducin casualties, thus increasing availability. The second woul eventually reduce the number of weld repairs in mai workshops and thus the time a locomotive was out service, but had a more limited effect on improvin availability.

Once the effects just mentioned had been seen to b working, the pressure was off and it soon became clea

that the other longer term benefits of the crankcase and cylinder block modifications did not continue to warrant the time and money spent on the crash programme. Money could in fact be saved by curtailing the programme with the additional benefit of releasing to traffic the eight locomotives previously held for the programme, and by return of the 17 spare engines to assist turnround in BR's Crewe Works.

It was agreed to curtail the Barrow programme at the 155th engine and to slow down the rate of modification in the first three months of 1967. The 155th locomotive was released at the end of March of that year and the six engines remaining at Barrow were fully overhauled, modified and delivered to Crewe by the beginning of June 1967. By 1 June 1967, a total of 190 engines had been modified at Barrow and a further 111 at Crewe, making a total of 301 out of the 527 12LDA28-C engines in being. Barrow continued to machine and fit the additional

Left: A white wilderness surrounds 47.550 as it heads the up 'Clansman' past Dalnaspidal on 2 February 1976. The train is formed of air-conditioned Mk 2 stock. / *D. E. Canning*

Below left: Large numbers of Inter-City expresses have remained in the charge of Class 47s throughout the 1970s. With Sulzer engine in full cry 47.429 lifts the 13.12 Sheffield-Edinburgh past Lamberton Beach on the Scottish Border. / *L. A. Nixon*

Below: Great Western trappings were still evident on Dainton Bank in 1972 as 1675 stormed to the summit with the 09.30 from Paddington. / *D. E. Canning*

balance weights to crankshafts and a shuttle service of crankshafts operated between Crewe, Derby and Barrow for the next three years.

To complete this chapter, mention should also be made of the replacement by BR of 168 of the 12LDA28-B and C cylinder blocks due largely to weaknesses brought about by corrosion. For replacement, a new design was made, eliminating weaknesses and potential weakness in the earlier version. In this connection, there were two areas where substantial improvement was possible viz the integral water supply pipe taking cooling water to the cylinder liners and the cantilevered support tray for the fuel pumps and cam followers. It is always the case that the structure of a reciprocating machine is subjected to forces which alternate because masses are either rotating or moving up and down, eg connecting rod big-ends rotate and pistons with connecting rod small ends reciprocate and, as previously mentioned, it is usually possible only to balance a proportion of such masses. In addition, in an internal combustion engine the reactions from the firing forces have to be distributed into the engine structure and, unless the structure is very rigid indeed, all of the forces mentioned produce deflections of the structure coupled with vibration.

In the case of the 12LDA28 engines, the cooling water supply pipe forms an internal structural member and is welded into a boss on both sides of each cast steel cross member. Additionally, plates are welded on each side which form the floor of the water space, so that the top side contains water and the underside forms the roof of the crankcase containing oil and oil mist. Where weight is of prime importance, as in a locomotive engine, rigidity has to be sacrificed to save weight and it is then usual to allow minute deflections of the structure vertically and horizontally and so it was in this case. To cut a long story short, certain welds in both the areas mentioned above were difficult to make and therefore of variable quality and opportunity was taken in the redesign to eliminate them altogether.

Now to the reasons for replacement of the 168 cylinder blocks. Cooling water treatment in diesel engines is quite common — ideally distilled water is the best possible coolant, but its use is not practical in large engines particularly in locomotives. Treatment of cooling water is carried out in a variety of ways for the following reasons:

1 To prevent scale formation
2 To minimise corrosion, particularly where some of the coolant is likely to absorb air. Rain water incidentally is particularly corrosive since it is rich in oxygen and carbon dioxide.

The cooling systems of some of the Class 47 locomotive (and all of the other Sulzer-engine locomotives) wer

Above left: Class 47s have long been a familiar sight on heavy block trains. In this 1969 view, D1647 was receiving rear end assistance from three Type 3s as it stormed the Lickey incline with a heavy coal drag. / *J. G. Glover*

Above: Class 47s are much used on merry-go-round operation of coal trains between colleries and power stations. To assist in this operation, where the train remains in motion during loading and unloading, some of the class have been fitted with a slow-speed control system. Here, 1915 rattles through Neath with empty mgr hoppers for Aberdare. / *J. H. Cooper-Smith*

nominally open to atmosphere in that coolant drained from the radiators into tanks when not in circulation.

Some operating Regions in BR were not convinced early enough of the need to use corrosion inhibitors, with the result that many of the Class 45 and 46 locomotive cylinder blocks suffered internal corrosion which developed in certain welds, notably the weld between side wall and top plate which, being stressed, developed a phenomenon called corrosion fatigue in which corrosion pits in the welds rapidly developed into fatigue cracks. In many cases water treatment arrested the trouble, but damage had been done which either limited the life or led to expensive repairs being necessary. When the Class 47 locomotives came into service the lesson had been learned the hard way and water treatment was applied from the beginning.

Soon after replacement of cylinder blocks on those Class 45 and 46 locomotives requiring it, the decision was made to introduce electric train heating and conversion of the Class 47 locomotives was under way soon after the first new Mark II cylinder blocks began to flow from the makers. In all 135 Class 47 locomotives were to be converted in addition to the 20 original locomotives D1500-19 (47.401-420). It was decided that as many as possible should have the new cylinder blocks instead of the Classes 45 and 46 because it was argued that locomotives fitted for electric heating would be engaged on the important Inter-City services which employed a high proportion of full power working (high load factor). Accordingly, exchange of Class 47 cylinder blocks between Crewe and Derby was made, the worst from Classes 45 and 46 being scrapped to be replaced by 'good' blocks from Crewe, in turn being replaced by new Mark II blocks.

One of the side benefits of the Mark II cylinder blocks has not so far been exploited, namely the extra stiffness imparted to the structure as a whole which, in almost every one of the areas previously under examination, results in still lower stress levels, or put another way, could safely enable engine speed to be raised again to 800rpm without exceeding the 'safety' levels laid down by BR. Understandably, the desire not to introduce yet another variant within the Class 47 fleet has weighed heavily against making the change.

6 The Electric Transmission

South of Lancaster, a Class 5 4-6-0 meets a Class 47 heading a train of the latest 100ton bogie tank wagons. / *C. Lofthus*

The transmission equipment of a diesel electric loco-motive, necessary to transmit the power of the diesel engine to the road wheels of the locomotive includes the traction generator and traction motors, gearing, sus-pension, etc. In Class 47 locomotives advantage has been taken of the gearing associated with the twin-bank engine with its two crankshafts to run the main traction generator at higher than crankshaft rpm. In fact, the gear ratio between crankshafts and output shaft is 1 : 1.44 so that when crankshaft revolutions are 800 the output shaft and generator run at 1,152rpm. This enables a slightly smaller and lighter machine to be employed than would have been the case if generator armature speed had been limited to 800rpm.

There are three main variations in the electrical generating equipment of the Class 47 fleet. The first 20 locomotives were designed to heat trains by steam or electricity and in consequence the main generator frame was lengthened to accommodate the stator of the train heating dc generator within the same frame. In fact the auxiliary generator is also part of the same unit, hence on locomotives 47.401-20 (D1500-19) the three generator armatures are mounted on a common cast steel hub which is solidly coupled at the train heating generator end to the diesel engine output shaft. Only a single self-aligning roller bearing supports the hub at the auxiliary generator end, the normal arrangement in diesel-electric practice. Some axial movement is provided to take account of expansion of the armature shaft and special labyrinth seals are fitted to exclude dirt and retain the lubricating grease (Fig 17).

The main or traction generator armature is the largest of the three machines and is built directly on to the hub. Both train heating and auxiliary generator armatures are built on to separate sleeves, either of which can be removed for attention without disturbing the main armature (see photo p51). When such large masses are rotating at relatively high speeds it is necessary to check that they are in proper dynamic balance, to which special attention is paid.

The magnets of main and train heating generators are assembled into one structure, manufactured from a special magnetic steel plate, rolled and welded to form a cylindrical frame. Feet welded to the structure rest on the engine crankcase side frame extensions. The auxiliary generator frame, which is of much smaller dimensions, is bolted to the front end plate of the main frame.

The generators are self-cooled by their own shaft-mounted fan which draws air through the auxiliary, main and train heating machines, discharging it downwards through the underframe at the coupling end. Access to the commutators and brushes is obtained through openings above each commutator and extra access is obtained by removal of the air inlet covers on the main end frame. Quick-release fastenings are provided where access for maintenance is required. Current to the traction motors is conducted through heavy cables sheathed with oil-resistant insulation. These can be readily disconnected when it is required to lift the generators or complete power unit out of the locomotive.

For the remainder of the fleet, the main generator frame is shorter, as there is no combined train heating

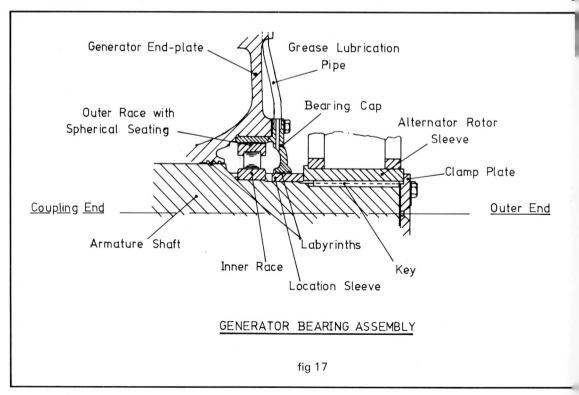

GENERATOR BEARING ASSEMBLY

fig 17

generator and the engine crankcase side arms are correspondingly shorter. The later conversions of locomotives for electric train heating employ an auxiliary alternator in place of the dc auxiliary generator. This is described later.

There are two main variations of traction generator, dependent upon whether traction motors are connected in three circuits of two in series or all in parallel but, in principle, the two machines are of similar construction, following the same lines as the combined three-machine unit of the first 20 locomotives. Electrically, the two variants are quite different. On the earlier series-parallel locomotives the traction generator has eight poles and a continuous rating of 2,130amps at 844 volts giving a power output of 1,797.7kw or at maximum voltage, 1,860amps, 970 volts giving 1,804.2kw. The all-parallel generator has 12 poles and the continuous rating is 4,260amps at 423 volts giving 1,801.9kw.

Both machines are built to the same standards as laid down for traction applications by the British Standards Institution, with high temperature insulation of all windings and commutators. The latter in the all-parallel generators are bigger and heavier than the series-parallel variant and it is a tribute to the designers of the later machine that its weight is only marginally greater.

Traction duty calls for almost continuous adjustment of generator excitation in order to match the engine power input and to maintain a substantially constant power input to traction motors for a given engine setting irrespective of train speed. The earlier generators are excited from the auxiliary generator, the adjustment to voltage being made by an engine governor-driven regulator to match engine and generator outputs by constant adjustment of a variable resistance unit. When the change to the all-parallel generator was made, opportunity was taken to change the method of generator excitation and the bulky regulator and resistances were replaced by an inductor alternator with two stator windings, bolted to the end of the auxiliary generator. The excitation current of the latter was small enough to be handled directly by a small wire-wound variable resistor, bolted direct to and driven from the oil vane motor in the engine governor.

The change from series-parallel to all-parallel was made for two reasons, ie to improve reliability and handling by the driver. As the same traction motors were employed with both variants the all-parallel generator operates at half the voltage of the series-parallel and thus reduces the possibility of flashover, particularly under wheel slip conditions. Additionally, the all-parallel connection limits the rise in voltage associated with the slipping of one axle and in turn reduces the possibility of other axles following suit. The advantages and disadvantages of the all-parallel arrangement may be summarised as follows:

Advantages

Low generator voltage (half)

Avoids sharp rises in voltage on traction motors in wheelslip conditions

Below: Main generator . / *Brush*

Disadvantages

Heavier, bulkier and more costly control gear required to handle the six circuits

High generator currents require large and costly commutator, brush gear and generator connections

Additional cabling required between control cubicle and traction motors.

The auxiliary generator, which does not really form part of the electric transmission may, however, be conveniently described here. It is a six-pole shunt-wound machine, the armature of which is mounted on a tapered extension of the main generator hub and is outboard of the main generator bearing. The frame is bolted direct to the main generator and carries the brush gear. On the all-parallel locomotives an inductor alternator is in turn carried from the auxiliary generator frames (see below). The output of the auxiliary generator is 55kw and the voltage is maintained at 110 over the normal operating speed range 485-1,155rpm. In the Class 47/4 locomotives, 47.421-47.555, the auxiliary dc generator has been replaced by an auxiliary/heating alternator, to be described later.

The six traction motors per locomotive, three on each bogie, are basically similar throughout the fleet (see photo p53). They are of the nose suspended, axle hung type,

each motor being rated to absorb continuously its share of the power output of the main generator, ie 300kw at 710amps or the same power at 762amps each for a one hour period.

The frame of the motor is a steel casting of high magnetic quality and there are four main poles. As in the vast majority of traction applications the motors are series wound — that is the same current passes through armature and field in series. Cooling is provided by air under pressure supplied from cooling fans situated within the locomotive body and some 2,000cu ft/min is passed through each motor. As with the main generator, high temperature insulation is employed and there is ample access to commutator and brush gear. The armature is carried on roller bearings lubricated by high melting-point grease. One bearing, at the commutator end, is designed to locate the armature shaft while the other bearing allows freedom for the shaft to expand longitudinally.

Below: Main and auxiliary generators with inductor alternator. / *Brush*

Right: Traction motor. / *Brush*

Below right: Resilient gearwheel and traction motor roller suspension unit on axle.

The drive to the wheels is at the opposite end to the commutator and is through a solid pinion with straight teeth. This mates with a gear-wheel having built-in resilience in that the rim is connected to the hub through 24 special rubber bushes to cushion the motor and gear teeth from rail shocks transmitted to the gear hub which is pressed on the axle (see photo p53).

The motor itself is suspended at one side from the bogie frame through resilient units attached to a 'nose' cast on the motor frame and at the other side is bolted direct to a roller bearing suspension sleeve which surrounds the axle. Thus half of the motor weight is unsprung, ie it is 'axle-hung'. Originally, in the first 50 locomotives the suspension unit was a solid tube but due to a change in the BR requirements for axles, and in order to retain standard motors, a split tube had to be adopted from the 51st locomotive (D1682-47096) onwards.

The change in axle specification was suggested by experience in other locomotives and railcars and in the event the requirements of standardisation severely limited the space available for the split suspension tubes and considerable trouble was experienced with fractures of the tubes themselves (never the axles of the first 50 loco-motives which the change was designed to prevent!).

The gears themselves are enclosed in robust cast aluminium cases which are split at their centres, the two halves being clamped together by steel bolts, securely locked. The cases contain special gear lubricant and

access for periodic attention is by means of magnetic filler caps.

The traction motors are connected electrically to the main generator by four flexible cables per motor, arranged for ready disconnection for bogie changing purposes and replacement in the event of damage.

It is convenient at this point to discuss electric train heating. As already mentioned, the original 20 locomotives were equipped for direct current electric train heating as well as steam heating of trains (as was the prototype BRCW/AEI/Sulzer locomotive *Lion*) because in 1961/2 consideration was being given to the extension of electric heating beyond the already electrified lines. Ten years later the decision to abandon steam heating was finally made and the expensive conversion of another 135 Class 47 locomotives (now 47/4) has been undertaken but with a different electrical system.

While building the main/auxiliary generator groups for the first 20 locomotives it was relatively simple to incorporate an 8-pole dc shunt-wound generator within the same frame — it had been done already on the 98 Class 33 locomotives for the Southern Region. However with a machine of that type it was only possible to obtain a controlled output over a limited range of engine speed (or generator shaft speed) and an output power of 320kw was possible over the speed range 690-1,150rpm (480-800 engine rpm). Below 690rpm, the voltage is progressively reduced from the controlled 800 volts

Above left: Main generator armature with rotor of auxiliary/train heating alternator. / *Brush*

Above: Main generator with auxiliary/heating alternator in position. / *Brush*

normally required for heating purposes so that the engine was arranged to idle at 480rpm when train heating was required. At other times the usual 340-350rpm engine idling speed still obtained.

In order not to run the train heating generator completely without load, a condition which often leads to commutator glazing and brush wear, the radiator fans and traction motor cooling fans on Nos D1500-1519 (47.401-20) were fed at 800 volts. However, when dual-heated rolling stock did not materialise, at least on the Eastern Region to which locomotives 47.401-20 were allocated, the engine idling control apparatus was removed and the driving controls standardised with the rest of the fleet. The slight reduction in voltage, now for fans only over the range, 485-690rpm (340-480 engine revs) was no disadvantage in the mainly passenger diagrams on which the locomotives were employed.

Some 10 years later, following a BR policy decision to abandon steam heating on Mk II passenger rolling stock and particularly on stock in which pressure ventilation or full air-conditioning was installed, a high voltage train supply became essential and the electric heating equipment on locomotives 47.401-420 again came into its own. The question of how to deal with the other 135 locomotives which now had to be equipped for electric heating was resolved by adopting the system already fitted experimentally to two of the later production locomotives with auxiliary dual-wound alternators D1960/1 (47.514/5) which had sufficient capacity to supply the locomotive auxiliaries and some 400kw of train heating load. The advantage is that there is only a relatively small increase in weight and length which is easily accommodated with a minimum of alteration to power unit and other equipment.

On the new conversions, the two windings occupy the same slots in the stator and hence are magnetically coupled so that one voltage regulator suffices for both outputs. There is no commutator or brush gear requiring maintenance and both ac outputs are easily rectified by the use of diodes. It is necessary to rectify the train heating output since the alternator produces polyphase, variable frequency (with engine speed) current and only two heater cables run throughout the train. In order to avoid complications with control gear, engine idling speed on Class 47/4 locomotives has been increased marginally to 385rpm so that the generator group turns at 560rpm, sufficient to give the required output from the auxiliary alternator (see photos above and on p54).

7 Control Gear

It has already been seen that there are two basic variants in the arrangement of traction motors in the Class 47 fleet, usually referred to as the 'series-parallel' and 'all-parallel' locomotives respectively.

The original design incorporated a series-parallel motor circuit arrangement, where the main generator feeds three parallel branches of two traction motors in series and each branch is fed through an electro-pneumatically operated power switch (EP contactor), reversing switch and isolating link. The arrangment was fairly common and had the advantage that main generator currents and hence power cabling were of fairly moderate proportions with maximum voltages in the 900-1,100 range. There are 107 locomotives of the 'series-parallel' type including the five which were formerly Class 48, 49 of Class 47/0 and 58 of Class 47/4. For the remaining 400 'all-parallel' locomotives there are six parallel circuits each with its own EP contactor, reverser and isolating link operating at the same current levels but at half the voltage of the series-parallel locomotives.

Engine starting is technically simple, merely using the main generator as a starter motor to turn the engine to a speed at which there is sufficient compression pressure to produce the required heat to ignite spontaneously the fuel injected into the cylinder. When starting the engine on the Class 47 locomotive the main generator is isolated from the traction motors and fed direct from the large capacity battery, the circuit being made through the battery isolating switch and two electro-magnetic contactors which, once the engine is motoring, open and isolate the battery from the traction circuits.

The main generator output regulator is flange-mounted to the engine governor. Its function is to match the generator output to the available engine power output at all engine speeds so that the driver has only one main power handle on his controller to manipulate in order to start his train from rest and therafter adjust the power according to the needs of the moment. For simplicity's sake, the driver's power handle, except for the first few degrees of angular movement, acts directly on the engine governor speed-setting element and power output is then regulated automatically for the speed set by the driver.

Right: The Class 47/3s are not fitted with train heating equipment and are normally confined to freight work. 47.302 is here leaving Wakefield with coal empties for Crofton on 18 July 1974. / *M. Mitchell*

Above: Control cubicle for series-parallel connected traction motors / *Brush*

Left: Driver's controls.

The bulk of the control gear is occupied with switching the main generator output current to the traction motors interlocking and safety circuits being incorporated to ensure the correct sequence of operation. For example, it would be disastrous to connect the starting battery to the main generator output when running under full power and interlocking circuits are provided to ensure the battery is not connected to the main generator at the same time as the traction motors and vice versa. Auxiliary apparatus such as air compressors, brake exhausters, battery charging, train heating boilers, etc, also need some control apparatus for switching on and off as required and most of the apparatus for controlling their respective motors is contained within the main control cubicle (see photo above).

A set of driving controls is situated in each driving cab (see photo left). The driver's controller is itself quite simple piece of equipment, consisting of two handles movement of which is suitably interlocked and a master lock operated by a small key, one of which is issued to ach driver for his personal retention. The reversing handle controls the motor reversing switches in the control cubicle as well as locking the main power handle when the cab is not in use. It has four positions — off, reverse, engine only, forward. 'Engine only' is the neutral position and enables the engine to be started and idled with all auxiliary apparatus running. It is used when the locomotive is stationary to allow the driver to release his safety device so that he can move across the cab or even leave it if necessary. The 'off' position normally leaves the engine running but locks the controls so that the driver may remove his master key to change his driving position end for end. Only certain auxiliary apparatus then remains in operation.

The main power handle controls the switches supplying power to the traction motors and adjusts the engine speed by supplying air through a regulating valve direct to a cylinder and piston in the engine governor. The automatic load regulator then adjusts the electrical power output of the generator to match the available engine power almost irrespective of locomotive running speeds. Originally there were six marked positions dividing the angle through which the power handle can be moved viz, 'off', '1', '2', '$\frac{1}{2}$', '$\frac{3}{4}$', 'full'. Positions 1 and 2 had locating notches which corresponded to two fixed electrical conditions which enabled shunting movements to be accomplished without using excessive engine power. Originally, locomotives D1500-19 (47.401-20) had a different arrangement. The power handles were provided with an extra position marked + to which the handle could be moved against a spring, the handle returning to the 'full' position on release. The idea was that, with train heating in operation, the full engine output of 2,750bhp would be available at the 'full' position and movement to the + position would cut-off the heating temporarily and give the driver the extra amount for traction for so long as the handle was held against the stop. When working non-electrically heated trains the engine output 'full' was limited to 2,500bhp at 760rpm. Again, the driver could obtain the full 2,750bhp by moving the handle to +, but this time it would be by increasing engine speed to 800rpm.

When subsequent locomotives were built, D1521 onwards, without electric train heating, it was decided to revert to the more normal arrangement and the + position was discarded. The 'full' position then gave 2,750bhp at 800rpm, power being reduced proportionally according to the angular position of the power handle, which is now marked 'off', '$\frac{1}{4}$', '$\frac{1}{2}$', '$\frac{3}{4}$', and 'full' only.

No provision was made for multiple operation, that is to say the coupling and control of two or more locomotives driven from one cab — probably a short-sighted decision as today there are many workings involving the use of two locomotives in tandem requiring the provision of two crews. The alterations which would now be involved in the fitting of the necessary apparatus are of such a magnitude as to make the task unattractive financially and practically.

Auxiliary Equipment

The so called auxiliary equipment of a diesel-electric locomotive can absorb from five to seven per cent of the gross engine output. Although termed auxiliary, the locomotive will not function without for example, air

Below: Use of the four-character headcode panel has been discontinued and many locomotives are now fitted with roller blinds carrying two white dots, or have had the display replaced by white lights. Unmodified locomotives should display four noughts as shown by 47.199 as it passes the ex-GWR station at Bramley on 27 June 1977. / *J. Scrace*

Above: A loaded Freightliner train from the docks leaves Southampton behind 47.145 on 2 April 1974. / *J. Scrace*

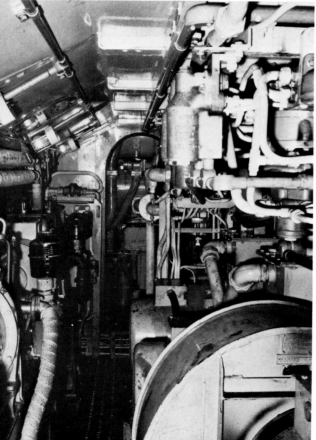

Left: Auxiliary compartment illustrating restricted access.

under pressure or at reduced pressure (vacuum) for brakes, cooling air for diesel engine and traction motors, nor will it be able to operate steam-heated passenger trains in winter without a properly functioning steam generator. All of this adds up to the need for the source of auxiliary power being as reliable as anything else. The auxiliary machines supplied from the auxiliary generator built into the main generator group include two traction motor ventilating blowers, two vacuum exhausters, either one or two air compressors, engine water circulating pump (also incorporating fuel supply pump and lubricating oil priming pump) and boiler fan and pump motor when fitted. The auxiliary generator also supplies current for battery charging, cab heating, operation of control gear and lights. The two latter take an alternative supply from the battery when the diesel engine is not running. The auxiliary generator absorbs about 90bhp.

In addition, the engine cooling equipment requires power for operating the radiator cooling fans. On locomotives 47.401-20 there are two electric-motor driven fans each absorbing about 32hp which are supplied from the train heating generator. On all subsequent locomotives cooling fans are driven by hydrostatic motors, direct from the diesel engine and absorb a total of 60hp. The total auxiliary load supplied from the engine of the Class 47 locomotives is therefore 150hp or about 5½% of the gross engine output. The

...oto bottom p60 shows the auxiliary compressor and ...ry close juxtaposition of components in this ...mpartment of the locomotive body.

No description of control gear would be complete ...thout reference to the electronic equipment employing ...lid state devices now available to railway engineers. At ...e time the Class 47 was conceived, railway engineers ...ere beginning to take an active interest in the ...ployment of solid state devices to replace conventional ...ectromagnetic equipment. After various trials it became ...ident that, provided reliability was at least equal there ...ere certain control applications for solid state devices ...hich could beneficially utilise 'transistorised' equipment. ...hile the majority of locomotives were built with the then ...nventional electromagnetic control equipment, many ...ve since been modified (some built originally) to employ ...lid state devices for the following functions: battery ...arging, automatic voltage regulation auxiliary ...nerators and train heating alternators, traction motor ...ld control, engine load regulation and automatic low ...eed control.

While solid state voltage regulators were probably the ...st area to be investigated, the requirement for handling ...erry-go-round trains at CEGB power stations led to the ...ed for an accurate indication of low speed which could ...ot be met by the conventional tacho-generator equip-...ent. Hawker Siddeley Dynamics, in association with ...rush produced a speed indicator which comprised a ...othed wheel and an inductive probe from which pulses ...e generated and fed into an electronic unit which is ...pable of indicating smoothly and accurately speeds as ...w as 0.5mph. Actually the same equipment feeds either ...e slow speed speedometer which is graduated 0-3mph, ...y operating a selector switch, or the normal speedometer ...hich covers the range 0-100mph.

The indicating equipment alone was thought to be ...fficient initially for merry-go-round operation but early ...ials soon showed that when loading or unloading trains, ...e attention of the driver was unduly monopolised by the ...ed to regulate the power in order to hold a constant ...eed against the continuously varying train load. ...onsequently the automatic speed control was developed ...nd has now been adopted. Now the driver merely selects ...low running', sets the slow running speed adjustment to ...e value required between 0.5 and 3.5mph and moves the ...ain power handle to the ¼ position. Trains speed is then ...utomatically maintained at the constant selected value ...respective of changes in gradient or load. The same ...eedometer equipment is utilised to provide signals for ...action motor field controls for the sequential operation ...f the divert stages at appropriate pre-set speeds.

As an extension of the slow-speed control, automatic ...ad regulation can also be incorporated and is fitted on ...me locomotives. The engine governor oil-vane motor, ...ready described elsewhere, is arranged to operate a ...osition transducer which provides a signal for a high ...utput stage control unit, thus matching generator ...xcitation to available engine output. Again, following ...om electronic control of load regulation, it is possible to ...corporate traction motor current limitation, thus aiding ...arting heavy trains when adhesion conditions are

difficult. Although not generally fitted to Class 47, trials have been carried out on some locomotives. Electronic load regulator units are now, however, fitted on the 404, 'all-parallel' locomotives.

The engine starting battery must of necessity be of large capacity and is recharged and kept charged by current supplied from the auxiliary generator. In order to prevent the battery discharging through the auxiliary generator when the engine is stopped, or should the generator fail to provide a sufficient voltage, the battery has to be disconnected when the generator-voltage falls below the battery voltage and it was the practice to provide a contactor controlled by a detector relay to protect the battery. Today, the relay and contactor, with all their moving parts are replaced by one static item, a diode, which permits current to flow into the battery from the auxiliary generator but not in the reverse direction, in other words an electrical non-return valve. Twelve or thirteen years ago diodes were in their infancy; today they are extremely reliable.

Below: 47.538 throws out a splendid exhaust trail as it climbs from the River Avon viaduct towards Kenilworth on the Leamington-Coventry line, with a block oil train. / *G. O. Swain*

8 How they are used

soon as the new Class 47 locomotive had demon-
ated its potential usefulness for a very wide range of
ties, regional operating authorities were clamouring for
allocation of them. During the time which elapsed
ween the first allocation to ER Finsbury Park depot in
uary 1963 and their appearance on Crewe-Perth
presses in February 1965, they had traversed almost
ry trunk line and most of the important secondary
es and their allocation was spread over a wide basis.
ey had been subjected to comprehensive loading and
er road tests, some made over critical sections such as
eter-Plymouth and the Lickey incline. No 47.401
tarted a trailing load of 690 tons twice on the 1 in 37.7
the Lickey in February 1963 and similarly made
starts from rest on the 1 in 38-43 of Dainton
nk with 17 coaches. However, on the whole, the
phasis on testing was more noticeable in the areas
ere the maximum weight of block loads required to be
ved in unit trains. Hence, soon after the appearance of
first locomotives, test mineral trains of more than
00 tons were to be seen running between Doncaster
d Scunthorpe, Doncaster and Thorpe Marsh and many
liery branches with heavy gradients. The Class 47 was
ver a glamour locomotive, and made an equally
uable contribution to the general working in the field of
vement of heavy freight as it did in being able to stand
for 'Deltics' and 'Westerns' on high speed passenger
rk.

As early as April 1963, the Class 47 locomotive had
made a significant impact on the working of both goods
and heavy freight between Peterborough and London. A
load equivalent to 75 wagons could be handled by one of
the new units over this section as compared with the
previous limit of 65 wagons using a steam locomotive or
a 2,000bhp diesel. An instance of the sort of economics
brought about by this higher haulage capacity is afforded
by the fact that by the remarshalling of loads and
sometimes adjusting the intermediate stops, it was found
possible to withdraw no less than six down Class 4 freight
trains which operated between various points bounded by
London and Doncaster.

Under a filthy sky Class 47/4 No 1518 heads for West
Burton Power station with empty fly-ash wagons, at Cow Paddle on
the Lincoln avoiding line. / Rev G. B. Wise

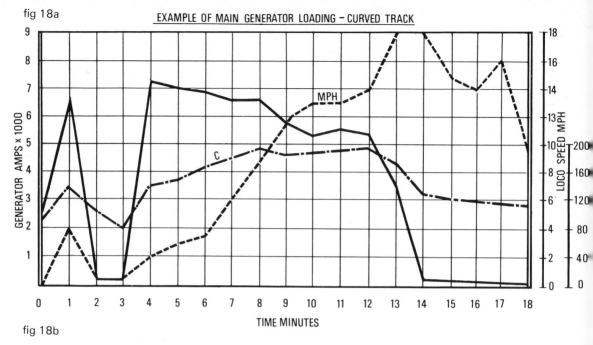

fig 18a

EXAMPLE OF MAIN GENERATOR LOADING – CURVED TRACK

fig 18b

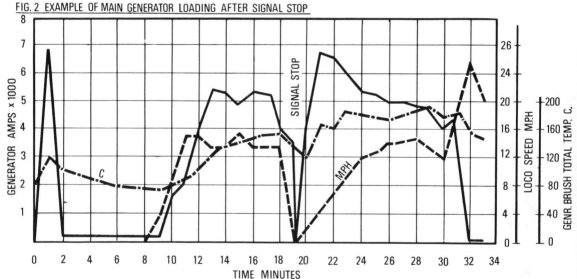

FIG. 2 EXAMPLE OF MAIN GENERATOR LOADING AFTER SIGNAL STOP

The new class of locomotive was introduced into the realm of heavier freight working at a time when the ER was about to adopt for the old GN line a simplified freight train classification system. This scheme provided for the seven different classes of freight train then extant to be reduced to two. One was to be the fully fitted express freight train with a normally maximum speed of 55mph rising to 60mph in special circumstances. (Needless to say at this time the spate of plain line derailments of short wheelbase four-wheeled wagons had not begun to rear its ugly head). The other category was to be a modification of the exisiting Class 7 train (express freight, livestock or ballast train not fitted with a continuous brake) which was permitted a maximum speed of 40mph. To run train of the same weight at higher average speed classification known as 7* was introduced. The maximum load was that which the hauling locomotive could star and accelerate on the steepest ruling gradient so as t clear the latter within the specified time during which th short term rating of the electrical traction machines coul be used. Its maximum speed was 35mph and, in order t narrow the gap between the average and the maximum speeds, a few wagons fitted with the vacuum brake an varying in number according to the total weight of th train were marshalled next to the locomotive in order t augment its own brake power.

In the earlier days of dieselisation, many railwaymen whose job did not require them to have a knowledge of heat transfer and the indestructibility of energy, found it difficult to understand why the brake power of a diesel locomotive with small wheels and superior hauling capacity was significantly less than that of the steam engine with its large wheels which it displaced. The Class 47 locomotive was a good example of such a diesel locomotive and its use on the 7* trains provided a useful increase in line capacity.

The introduction of the 7* classification on selected sections of the ER caused the operating authorities on other regions to have a closer look to see whether the way in which the potential of their share of the rapidly expanding fleet of Class 47 locomotives was being exploited to the best advantage. For instance, the WR soon tumbled to the fact that strict adherence to the electrical ratings and the time during which they could be used was imposing wasteful load limitations on some routes. An example of such a restriction was to be found in the Margam-Severn Tunnel Junction section. Leaving Margam marshalling yards in the up direction, a train is faced with a succession of rising gradients culminating in about 1½ miles at 1 in 92 between Pyle and the summit before Stormy Down. The latter short section had the effect of limiting by 20% the maximum load which could otherwise have been conveyed over some 53 miles of a route which carried a very heavy freight traffic interspersed with inter-city passenger trains. By the time that a train with a load which could easily be conveyed

over the rest of the route had reached the commencement of the 1 in 92 gradient west of milepost 196, its speed had fallen so that the hourly rating of the electrical equipment would be exceeded before it reached Stormy. Special tests were carried out to establish the degree of additional heating set up in the electrical machines if the full 'official' load + 20% was taken. It was found that if the overloading did not occupy more than 10min, the rise in temperature was acceptable and thus an unpublicised 10min rating came into being which was never abused, although some engineers were, understandably, apprehensive that it might be. The maximum loading was increased to take account of the new parameters and a useful increase in line capacity resulted (Fig 18).

As an indication of the load hauling potential of the Class 47s in difficult circumstances, a log of a freight train grossing 1,120 tons behind the locomotive running from Margam Moors to Stormy Down is shown with the corresponding gradient profile in Fig 19.

Occasionally, a problem would arise when new traffic patterns were initiated and heavy trains were routed over lines little used, perhaps for years, and which in any case had never carried trains of the weight made possible by Class 47 haulage. When in April 1966, heavy freight trains began running between Swindon and Temple Mills worked by Swindon and Stratford men respectively, the display of pyrotechnics caused by the slipping of Class 47s when trains in the up direction between Neasden Junction, Dudding Hill Junction and Cricklewood where in the hands of men to whom the route and type of

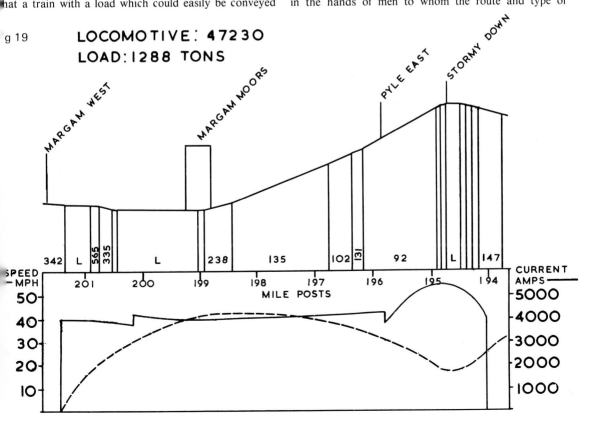

Fig 19

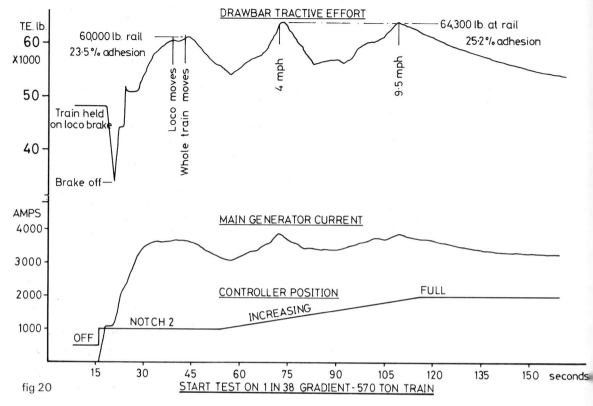

DRAWBAR TRACTIVE EFFORT

60,000 lb. rail
23.5% adhesion

64,300 lb. at rail
25.2% adhesion

Train held on loco brake

Brake off—

Loco moves

Whole train moves

4 mph

9.5 mph

T.E. lb.
60
X1000

50

40

AMPS
4000

MAIN GENERATOR CURRENT

3000

2000

CONTROLLER POSITION

FULL

INCREASING

1000

OFF

NOTCH 2

15   30   45   60   75   90   105   120   135   150   seconds

fig 20   START TEST ON 1 IN 38 GRADIENT-570 TON TRAIN

working was new, was something to be remembered. The incline was severe and the section of line had been little used for some two years and there were several layers of rust to remove from the rails. Resort was made to banking for about three days, during which every man in the links concerned was specially tutored in the handling of the locomotive over the critical section. The working quickly settled down without assisting locomotives. Enginemen are very quick on the uptake when their professional competence encounters a situation of this kind.

It was in the realm of block train movement of the 'merry-go-round' type, however, where Class 47 locomotives were probably subjected to the most severe tests of their traction machinery. Many colliery branches were laid with some notorious curves and the gradients of some had become more severe over the years, due to subsidence, than appeared from an examination of surveyors' charts when constructed. Signals, the position of which were logical and acceptable in relation to the original alignment, had in certain cases become places at which a train could be stopped but from which it could be restarted sometimes only with great difficulty, during which time rapid heating of main generator brushes and commutator risers could occur. In Fig 18 is shown an example of the temperatures reached by the main generator brushes of a Class 47 locomotive when starting from a signal stop at the commencement of a rising gradient of 1 in 115 with a trailing test load of 1,550 tons. In this instance, the start was smooth without slipping,

but required a current of 6,800A falling to 4,500A after nine minutes during which time the main generator brush temperature reached 193°C and some 149°C test paint on the commutator risers of the generator was thrown. The test load was considered excessive and was reduced by 5% for normal operation whilst investigation was made to see if it was practicable to move the signal, which was the only impediment on this branch to movement of the full test load without endangering the machinery of the locomotive.

Exertion of maximum tractive effort at starting is often accompanied by wheelslip, particularly when adhesion between wheel and rail is low due to climatic or other conditions. If wheelslip is severe and not promptly arrested, burning of the rails results and if excessive may well necessitate their renewal. Fig 20 shows a trace of the tractive effort at the drawbar of a Class 47 locomotive whilst starting a heavy train on a greasy rail. It is evident that the driver was trying to accelerate the train without exceeding main generator current limitations, but repeated wheelslips, although of only short duration resulted in lowering the rate of acceleration which in turn required even higher tractive effort peaks to keep the train moving until wheelslip ceased.

Despite sophisticated wheelslip detection and correction systems allied to intensive driver training, the kind of occurrence outlined in the preceding paragraph was, and is, more frequent because the Class 47 locomotives, alone amongst all BRs diesel locomotives, are not fitted with the means of interposing an abrasive material, such s sand or 'fines' between the wheel and rail. When the surface of the rail is 'greasy' after becoming contaminated from external sources, it may be found that there in insufficient adhesion between wheel and rail to support the tractive effort necessary to move a heavy train from rest and accelerate it. The train either remains where it is or has to be divided or assisted, none of these situations being popular with the operator nor, indeed, with the civil engineer if rail burns are caused by severe wheelslip.

Nobody detests wheelslip more than a conscientious driver and some ER drivers in the early days would not take out a Class 47 locomotive without some abrasive fines contained in small bags carried on the footplate. In the event of very poor adhesion conditions being encountered, the secondman would descend to the ballast with his bag of abrasive material and distribute it carefully and frugally over the rails ahead of the locomotive before the driver made another attempt to move the train. The ruse usually succeeded but was not encouraged by authority since the presence of abrasive material loosely stowed in the cab of a machine so susceptible to the influence of dirt was hardly appropriate.

Although operators and civil engineers throughout BR bemoaned the occasional lapses of the Class 47s in the field of heavy freight movement as recorded above, they did not find it possible to justify the considerable expenditure necessary to fit sanding apparatus retrospectively to more than 500 locomotives. The fact appears to be that the number of days in a year which produced weather conducive to very low adhesion conditions together with the number of locations at which these conditions were liable to be critical on any given day were, in total, insufficient to amount to a serious operating embarrassment. Support for this conclusion lies in the number of heavy diesel locomotives to be seen running about without their sanding apparatus being in working order, or without sand (of fines) in the receptacles provided.

It would, of course, have been a very different story if excessive wheelslip of diesel locomotives was a serious feature of passenger train operation in this country. But it is not and as more sophisticated electronic means have developed to detect wheelslip and apply automatic correction by closely controlling the reapplication of tractive effort, it now seems unlikely that the Class 47 fleet will ever be fitted with sanding apparatus. Nevertheless, experiments continue in an effort to devise an effective sanding apparatus at reasonable cost.

The merry-go-round trains between collieries and power stations comprise a set of about 30 wagons, not normally split and with load capacity of about 1,000 tons of coal, these figures being increased where route characteristics permit. On arrival at a power station, the train proceeds round a loop line (thus obviating the need

Below: 47.155 takes the Greenford line at West Ealing with a block oil train. The standard information stencil is visible below the locomotive number. / *N. E. Preedy*

for reversing) and whilst continuing to move at about 0.5mph, coal is discharged from the wagons into undertrack hoppers, this operation being activated by automatic discharge apparatus.

To obtain the consistently low and constant speed necessary during the automatic wagon discharge operation, an additional speedometer which would give a steady reading down to 0.2mph was fitted to selected Classs 47 locomotives. Although by using manual control of the locomotive it was found possible to move at and maintain very low speeds, the visual load on the driver in watching the speedometer and other instruments in an effort to regulate the power so as to maintain a constant speed against a continually decreasing resistance as the wagons emptied, proved somewhat demanding. An automatic speed control was therefore developed to improve this aspect of operation. The rail speed signal is taken from a toothed wheel bolted to the end of an axle in close proximity to an inductive probe pick-off mounted on the corresponding axlebox cover. The frequency output from the pick-off, which will obviously be proportional to the speed of rotation of the axle, is

converted to a dc voltage which is fed to moving coil speed indicating instruments of which there are two in each cab, one reading from 0.3mph, the other from 0 to 100mph.

When the locomotive is required to operate under slow speed control, the slow running switch is set to the appropriate cab, this connecting the power supply to the slow speed control unit. The speed demand potentiometer is then set to the selected speed and the main power controller handle moved to the quarter-power position. The train speed as the discharging operation takes place is now held at the value selected in the range from 0.3 to 3mph irrespective of changes in the total train resistance.

The ER pursued the principle of automation even further in the working of merry-go-round trains by initiating an experiment at Eggborough power station.

Below: One of the present headcode panel variations is shown by 47.157 as it runs into Hungerford with ARC stone hoppers bound for Westbury on 19 May 1977. / *G. F. Gillham*

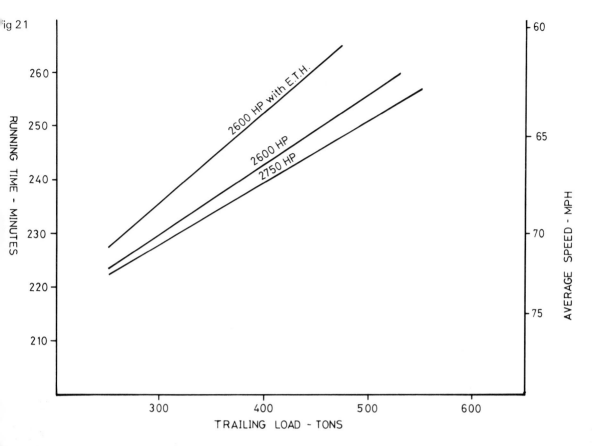

Fig 21

This allowed for the remote control of the locomotive during wagon discharge operations, as it appeared at the time that certain operating cost benefits might accrue if it was possible to 'remove' the driver from active participation in the train unloading operation without providing a relief driver. Between the rails of the length of track over which the locomotive was to run under remote control, a single core cable was laid in a loop into which a low current carrier wave signal was continuously transmitted. Low frequency command information was transmitted into the loop via the carrier, the resultant radiated signal being received by an aerial mounted on a bogie of the locomotive. The information thus received was then decoded into a specific locomotive control function.

The modus operandi was that a loaded train arriving at the power station from the colliery stopped at the signal in advance of the wagon weighbridge. The driver turned a switch on the locomotive from local to remote control and also set the appropriate slow speed control switch and the main power controller to one quarter full power position, as already described. The manually operated locomotive and train brake handles were placed by the driver in the release position, although the brakes continued to be held in the on position by the remote control system. The driver could now effectively retire from the scene, but in fact, remained on the locomotive to act in an emergency.

The train now became virtually in charge of the CEGB attendant at the discharge hopper console. When he was ready for the train to move over the hoppers, he pressed the 'train-go' button on the console and command information was transmitted to the locomotive via the loop conductor and the receiver on the locomotive. On receipt of the command, brakes were released and power applied simultaneously and the train proceeded, in this case at a pre-set speed of 1km/h. If the CEGB representative required the train to stop (eg in the case of defective wagon discharge gear) he simply removed the command signal, which was also effected automatically if the locomotive ran off the end of the track conductor.

Class 47, No 1979 (47.277) was the locomotive fitted with the experimental equipment which was operated for sufficient occasions to demonstrate that the principle of remote control could be applied in this way.

Another variation from the standard Class 47 locomotive was seen in No 1938 (47.258) which was fitted for push-pull working in order to assess the value of this type of operation at certain terminal stations.

The introduction of electric heating of coaching stock has, of course, detracted from the performance of the Class 47s fitted for this duty during the heating season because there is less tractive effort available at the drawbar. The graphs reproduced herewith (Fig 21) give some idea of the effect of the electric heating load on loads and running times.

9 Performance in Passenger Service

A chapter devoted to the performance of Class 47 locomotives in passenger service is a natural corollary to the matters discussed in Chapter 8. Although the performance of Class 47 locomotives in passenger service has been widely reported in the technical and popular railway press, a few examples of their exploits are included here. It should be emphasised that the Class 47s are mixed-traffic machines and although mechanically able to run at speeds up to 95mph, their tractive characteristics are such that the power available at the drawbar, substantially constant from 10mph, reduces progressively from 2,100 at 75mph to 1,760 at 95mph. It is hardly surprising, therefore that when a Class 47 has to deputise for a 'Deltic', for example, there is a lower level of performance and maximum attained speeds are lower, with the Class 47 being driven much harder, ie full engine revolutions have to be employed over a longer period than would be the case with a 'Deltic' operating to normal schedules. Fig 22 (over page) illustrates the point. The reason for the unloading of the main generator at the higher speeds is that the back electro-motive force of the traction motors rises with speed, a phenomonon well known to electrical engineers. This falling off in power output with increasing speed is accompanied also by constantly increasing internal and external tractive resistance of the locomotive, which again reduces the drawbar horsepower.

The principal difference between freight and passenger working is that with the former, high power outputs are required mainly to accelerate trains from rest and to move heavy loads up gradients, but the loads are limited by the available adhesion, ie the total weight on the rails of the locomotive, whereas with passenger trains, the power is utilised to maintain fast point-to-point timings. Liner trains come into a category somewhere in between as the loads are moderate (by freight standards) but point-to-point timings can be such as to demand relatively high power outputs continuously within a 75mph maximum permitted speed. In other words, freight trains require a high standard of handling but have a relatively low load factor (load factor = the proportion of 'on power' working to the total journey time), whereas the

Left: Pairings of Class 47s can produce a very lively ride! The 13.15 to Swansea waits to leave Paddington behind D1666 and D1754 on Easter Sunday 1966. / *D. E. Canning*

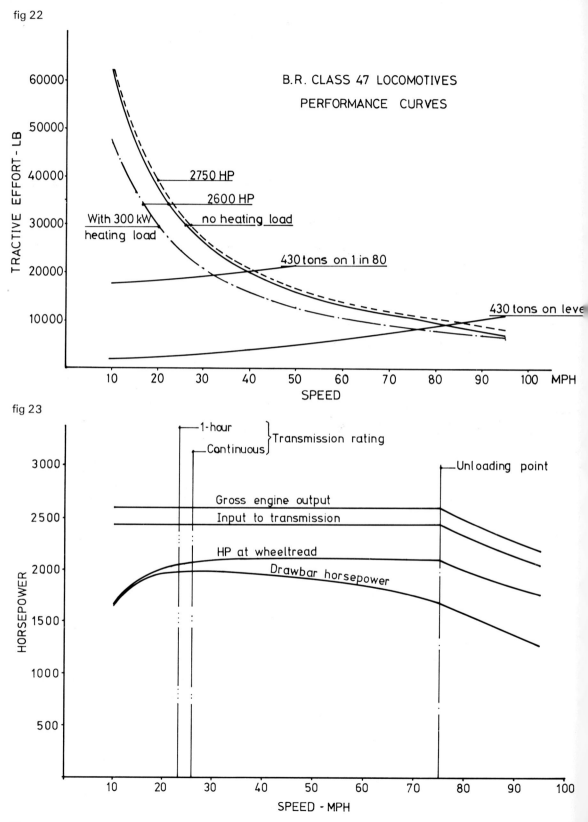

fig 22

B.R. CLASS 47 LOCOMOTIVES
PERFORMANCE CURVES

2750 HP

2600 HP
no heating load

With 300 kW
heating load

430 tons on 1 in 80

430 tons on leve

TRACTIVE EFFORT - LB

60000
50000
40000
30000
20000
10000

10 20 30 40 50 60 70 80 90 100 MPH
SPEED

fig 23

1-hour
Transmission rating
Continuous

Unloading point

3000

Gross engine output
Input to transmission

2500

HP at wheeltread
Drawbar horsepower

2000

HORSEPOWER

1500

1000

500

10 20 30 40 50 60 70 80 90 100
SPEED - MPH

72

majority of passenger work produces a high load factor, highest if lost time is being made up, or if working a train which is scheduled normally for a more powerful locomotive.

Steam locomotives had an inherent attribute in that, within limits, performance could be increased in service for short periods by drawing upon the considerable thermal storage capacity of the water in the boiler and the fire in the grate, generally to the detriment of the fireman. Schedules were usually calculated and then developed by trial and error to conform to levels of performance reasonably attainable from the locomotives normally employed, in average mechanical condition and fired at rates which could by physically sustained in normal everyday conditions consistent with the length of journey involved. With diesel and electric traction, performance is limited to well-defined maxima determined in the first case by the governed maximum output of the diesel engine and in the second by the capacity and characteristics of traction motors fed from a supply system at a substantially constant voltage.

As a rule, diesel engine output remains substantially the same over the period between successive overhauls — 2½ to 3 years — unless there is some major defect. For example, if one fuel injection pump becomes defective engine power output is reduced by rather more than $\frac{1}{12}$th in the case of the Class 47, which is certainly enough to cause comment even without the noticeable roughness of the engine which would be quickly detected by the enginemen. Actually the figures of horsepower quoted would be rather less because a certain amount of power would be required to drive the 'dead' piston and connecting rod etc. On the other hand, ironically enough, normal wear has a tendency to increase engine power output marginally and might well be detected as enhanced locomotive performance.

Schedules for all passenger trains are carefully computed from accurate performance data established from design and track tests. An excellent article by Group Captain J. N. C. Law appeared in *Railway World* for August 1973 which highlights the factors involved and the relevant data for the Class 47s is shown in Fig 23. In order that due allowance for the inevitable pw slacks is included, calculations are made for certain specific loadings on a flat-out basis taking all permanent speed restrictions into account and make-up time is then added. The method varies from Region to Region, but the result is that some 5 to 10% is added overall to the flat-out performance.

Today schedules have again been adjusted (or loads reduced) to take account of the lower tractive power available when air-conditioning and train heating is fed from the engine through the auxiliary alternators fitted to the Class 47/4s (see Fig 21). Such demands vary with ambient temperature and number of vehicles so that once again performance variations will be noted by recorders from time-to-time (day-to-day even) according to train internal-services demands.

By kind permission of the publishers a selection of runs recorded in tabular form by competent observers and taken from articles in *Modern Railways* and *Railway World* by that notable figure, the late Cecil J. Allen, is discussed below.

Table 1 WR Paddington-Exeter

Locomotive: Class 47 Co-Co Diesel No 1922 (2,750hp)
Load: 12 coaches, 393 tons tare, 430 tons gross

Dist		Schedule		Actual	Speeds
miles		A min	B min	min sec	mph
0.00	PADDINGTON	0	0	0.00	—
1.25	Westbourne Park	—	—	2.44	47
				sigs	*35
5.70	Ealing Broadway	—	—	8.06	69
9.10	SOUTHALL	9½	10½	10.57	75
13.25	West Drayton	—	—	14.00	86
18.45	SLOUGH	16	17½	17.33	91
24.25	Maidenhead	20	21½	21.30	85
31.00	Twyford	24½	26½	26.04	90
36.00	READING	28½	30½	30.20	*38
37.85	Southcote Junc	31	33	32.51	56
41.30	Theale	—	—	35.47	80
46.75	Midgham	—	—	40.07	*69
49.55	Thatcham	—	—	42.30	76
51.10	NEWBURY	43½	46½	45.14	81/82
58.50	Kintbury	—	—	49.16	78
61.55	Hungerford	—	—	51.48	*64
66.40	Bedwyn	54	58	55.42	77
70.10	Savernake	—	—	59.16	*59
75.35	Pewsey	(†2)	(†2)	63.14	90/86
78.90	Woodborough	65½	70	65.41	88
81.10	Patney	(†2)	(†2)	67.08	91
86.90	Lavington	73	77½	70.58	91
91.40	Edington	—	—	74.03	—
				pws	*50
94.55	Heywood Road Junc	78	82½	77.02	—
97.00	Fairwood Junc	80	84½	79.26	72
100.25	Clink Road Junc	82½	87	82.15	69
102.30	Blatchbridge Junc	84	88½	83.52	79
106.40	Witham	—	—	87.02	77
108.25	Brewham	—	—	88.30	73/82
111.70	Bruton	—	—	91.21	*68/89
115.15	CASTLE CARY	94	99	93.53	*75
120.05	Keinton Mandeville	—	—	97.32	85/82
122.30	Charlton Mackrell	—	—	99.06	84
125.55	Somerton	—	—	101.33	*72
130.80	Curry Rivel	—	—	105.21	88
				pws	*19
134.75	Athelney	—	—	109.13	—
138.00	Cogload	—	—	113.34	69/82
142.75	TAUNTON	116	121	117.28	*60
144.70	Norton Fitzwarren	—	—	119.12	74
149.85	Wellington	—	—	123.21	73
153.60	Whiteball	124½	132	126.58	56
156.90	Sampford Peverell	—	—	129.32	90
158.70	TIVERTON JUNC	—	—	130.48	80
160.90	Cullompton	(†3)	(†3½)	132.23	85/*73
165.10	Hele	—	—	135.35	85
170.10	Stoke Canon	—	—	139.00	90
172.25	Cowley Bridge Junc	141	149	140.47	*63
173.50	EXETER	143	151	142.57	—

*Speed restriction   †Recovery time (min)
A Schedule with 300 tons tare limit
B Schedule on summer Saturdays
Net time, 137min

Table 2 SC&ER Edinburgh-Newcastle
Locomotive: Class 47 Co-Co Diesel No 1619 (2,750hp)
Load: 12 coaches, 399 tons tare, 435 tons gross

Dist miles		Sched min	Actual min sec	Speeds mph	Dist miles		Sched min	Actual min sec	Speeds mph
0.00	EDINBURGH	0	0.00	—	78.30	Chathill	—	69.00	88
3.00	Portobello	4½	4.13	*45	81.20	Christon Bank	—	71.07	82
6.10	Monktonhall Junc	8	8.55	73	85.00	Little Mill	—	73.55	75/81
9.45	Prestonpans	—	11.43	79	89.60	ALNMOUTH	77	77.35	*60
13.20	Longniddry	—	14.29	80½	92.50	Warkworth	—	80.19	72
17.75	DREM	16½	17.50	86½	95.90	Acklington	—	83.03	75½
20.00	Milepost 20	—	19.24	87	98.10	Chevington	—	84.44	79
23.40	East Linton	—	21.55	*74	101.20	Widdrington	—	87.13	74
29.10	DUNBAR	25½	26.40	*58	103.50	Milepost 20	—	89.44	79
33.90	Innerwick	—	30.56	77	105.90	Pegswood	—	90.49	68½
36.45	Cockburnspath	—	33.07	70	107.85	MORPETH	92	92.59	*42
41.15	Grantshouse	38	37.38	61	110.55	Stannington	—	95.58	69
46.25	Reston Junc	—	42.11	72	114.00	Milepost 10½	—	98.43	78
51.85	Burnmouth	—	46.58	68½	116.75	Annitsford	(†3)	101 48	85½
57.45	BERWICK	52½	52.19	*35	119.45	Forest Hall	—	103 43	83
60.85	Scremerston	—	55.55	60	121.75	Benton Bank	—	105 29	*76
65.85	Beal	—	59.30	85½	124.45	NEWCASTLE	112	109.55	—
72.80	Belford	65	64.50	75					
75.80	Lucker	—	67.08	82					

*Speed restriction   †Recovery time (min)

The run in Table 1 was made with the down 'Cornish Riviera' on a summer Saturday and is notable for showing the capabilities of the locomotive without exceeding speed restrictions. The downhill speeds were even somewhat restrained, but speeds on the level and uphill showed that the locomotive was being worked at or near to maximum capacity with this 430 tons gross load when it was necessary to do so.

Table 2 shows an excellent example of a Class 47 deputising for a 'Deltic' on the up 'Flying Scotsman' loading to 435 tons gross which was within six tons of the maximum laid down for a 'Deltic' on the schedule shown. Table 2 in conjunction with a chart of the gradient profiles shows that the driver knew how to extract the last ounce of power from his steed and was able to bring the train into Newcastle two minutes early. It is noteworthy that the locomotive could never reach its maximum speed, but could maintain excellent times uphill (see photo below).

Above right: An unusual combination seen in Twyford cutting on 17 April 1969 in which 1678 piloted 'Western' class diesel-hydraulic D1024 on a down express. / G. P. Cooper

Below: An early Class 47 on an ER express. / BR

Table 3 ER Hitchin–Leeds
Locomotive: Class 47 Co-Co Diesel No D1874
Load: 8 coaches, 276 tons tare, 290 tons gross

Dist miles		Sched min	Actual min sec	Speeds mph	Dist miles		Sched min	Actual min sec	Speeds mph
0.00	HITCHIN	‡0	‡0.00	80	101.85	Milepost 133¾	—	72.53	85
5.20	Arlesey	—	3.13	98/96				pws	*25
9.25	Biggleswade	—	5.43	102	106.70	RETFORD	78½	77.15	—
12.25	Sandy	7½	7.32	94	112.05	Ranskill	—	83.20	86½
15.60	Tempsford	—	7.32	96	115.80	Bawtry	—	86.34	*60
19.85	St Neots	—	12.20	90	117.85	Milepost 149½	(†3)	88.15	68
24.05	Offord	—	15.13	*69	119.45	Rossington	—	89.33	82
26.95	HUNTINGDON	17	17.35	83½	121.30	Black Carr Junc	—	91.15	*60/65
30.10	Milepost 62	—	19.54	82	124.05	DONCASTER	96½	94.00	*45
35.45	Connington South	—	23.24	100	125.75	Bentley Crossing	98½	96.16	—
37.45	Holme	(†2)	24.47	*75	128.80	Adwick Junc	101½	98.57	71½
40.70	Yaxley	—	27.33	*70	132.70	South Elmsall	—	102.14	69
43.10	Fletton Junc	—	29.24	—	135.85	Hemsworth	—	104.48	77½
44.45	PETERBOROUGH	33	31.20	*26	140.00	Hare Park Junc	111½	108.18	*64/79
47.60	Werrington Junc	37	34.47	72	143.90	WAKEFIELD	116½	112.32	—
52.95	Tallington	—	38.43	82				pws	*20
56.75	Essendine	43½	41.17	90/85	2.75	Lofthouse N. Junc	—	5.08	54
60.35	Little Bytham	—	43.42	88/83½	4.30	Ardsley	6	6.57	51
65.20	Corby Glen	—	47.12	85	6.60	Beeston Junc	(†3)	8.58	74
68.20	Stoke	51	49.23	82	8.50	Geldard Road Junc	13½	11.18	*20
70.20	Great Ponton	—	50.48	92				sig.stop	*0
73.55	GRANTHAM	55	53.07	*70	10.30	LEEDS CITY	19	16.45	—
77.80	Barkston S. Junc	58	56.03	92					
83.45	Claypole	—	59.39	102					
88.20	NEWARK	64½	62.56	*80					
91.05	Bathley Lane	—	65.16	*69					
95.55	Crow Park	—	68.23	92					
99.30	Dukeries Junc	—	71.03	83½					

*Speed restriction   †Recovery time (min)   ‡Passing time

Note: The train passed Hitchin 19½min late due to brake trouble compelling a stop at Potters Bar, also a 15mph pw check at Hatfield and a 52mph signal check at Wymondeley

Table 4 LMR Hellifield-Carlisle

Locomotive: 2,580hp

Class 47 No		D1844		D1949	
Load: Coaches/tons tare/gross		10/364/385		12/429/460	
Dist	Sched	Actual	Speeds	Actual	Speeds
miles	min	min sec	mph	min sec	mph
0.0 HELLIFIELD	0	0.00	—	0.00	—
1.2 Long Preston	—	2.19	55	2.28	56
3.2 Settle Junc	4	4.13	68	4.24	66
5.2 SETTLE	—	6.05	60	6.18	59
9.6 Helwith Bridge	—	10.51	53/58	11.09	52/57
11.3 Horton	—	12.36	55	12.56	54
13.6 Selside	—	15.08	53	15.31	52
16.0 Ribblehead	—	17 51	52/54	18 16	51/54
17.2 Blea Moor	25	19.14	52	19.41	51
22.1 Dent	—	23.53	75/*70	24.24	72/*69
25.4 Garsdale	—	26.36	83	27.06	76
28.4 Ais Gill	36	28.57	75	29.42	66
32.0 Mallerstang	—	31.31	88/*78	32.29	83/*73
35.3 Kirkby Stephen	—	33.57	83	35.03	90
38.5 Crosby Garrett	—	36.28	*73	37.35	*74
43.5 Ormside	—	40.17	87	41.27	83
46.0 APPLEBY	50	42.04	78	43.24	70/78
				pws	*35
49.0 Long Marton	—	44.12	88	45.56	—
		sigs	*45		
53.4 Culgaith	—	48.06	—	50.49	80
57.0 Langwathby	—	51.17	78	53.37	74
59.5 Long Meg Sidings	—	53.09	83	55.32	81
61.3 Lazonby	—	54.32	76	56.58	74
63.7 Milepost 295	—	56.26	72	58.55	72
66.8 Armathwaite	—	58.38	90	61.18	81
68.4 Low House	—	59.51	*70	62.32	*65
71.7 Howes Sidings	—	62.29	80	65.19	74
		pws	*70	pws	*50
74.1 Scotby	—	64.27	78	67.43	69
75.9 Petteril Bridge Junc	76	66.25	*25	70.06	*25
76.8 CARLISLE	78	68.30	—	72.50	—
76.8 Net times (min)	78	67¼	—	71¾	—

*Speed restriction

Table 5 ScR Carlisle-Glasgow

Locomotive: Class 47 Co-Co Diesel No D1848 (2,750hp)
Load: 11 coaches, 397 tons tare, 420 tons gross

Dist		Sched	Actual	Speeds
miles		min	min sec	mph
0.00	CARLISLE	0	0.00	—
2.00	Kingmoor	—	3.44	56
4.05	Rockcliffe	—	5.44	64
7.50	Milepost 7½	—	8.25	78
8.60	Gretna Junc	9½	9.23	75
12.85	Kirkpatrick	—	12.52	72
14.50	Milepost 14½	—	14.09	69½/75
16.60	Kirtlebridge	(†5)	16.18	—
			pws	*30
20.00	Ecclefechan	—	20.30	58
22.00	Milepost 22	—	22.30	62
25.65	LOCKERBIE	29½	25.36	79½
28.55	Nethercleugh	—	27.45	85
31.60	Dinwoodie	—	30.06	74
34.40	Wamphray	—	32.19	79½
39.60	BEATTOCK	41½	36.20	73
42.00	Milepost 42	—	38.20	61
44.00	Milepost 44	—	40.33	50
46.00	Milepost 46	—	43.13	42
48.00	Milepost 48	—	46.07	40
49.60	Beattock Summit	57	48.42	40/77
52.50	Elvanfoot	—	51.25	73/68
55.15	Crawford	—	53.38	75/76½
57.70	Abington	—	55.43	73/69
63.10	Lamington	(†5)	60.04	79½
66.80	Symington	—	62.52	73
68.45	Thankerton	—	64.10	77
73.50	CARSTAIRS	82	68.30	*48
76.25	Cleghorn	85	71.38	60
			pws	*12
78.45	Criagenhill	—	75.00	—
80.65	Braidwood	—	77.16	75
81.90	Carluke	—	78.15	77/82
84.00	Law Junc	92½	80.22	*40
86.40	Wishaw South	—	82.52	75½
88.25	Flemington	—	84.16	79½
89.40	MOTHERWELL	97½	85.23	*58
93.80	Uddingston	101½	89.02	79½
95.65	Newton	103	90.30	69
97.20	Cambuslang	(†2)	92.00	—
98.30	Rutherglen Junc	107	93.04	*55
			pws	*24
101.25	Eglinton Street	110½	98.00	—
102.25	GLASGOW CENT	113	100.24	—

*Speed restriction   †Recovery time (min)

The exploits of another Class 47 deputising for a 'Deltic' on the ER are shown in Table 3 on a down Kings Cross-Leeds express as from Hitchin. The schedule is not an easy one, even for a 'Deltic'. Yet the driver of No 1874 improved on this very fast schedule by no less than 10min net, another convincing proof of the versatility of the Class 47.

When hill climbing at high average speed is the order of the day, the Class 47 again comes into its own. Table 4 shows how Nos 1844 and 1949 respectively tackled that bête-noire of steam days, the long grind from Settle Junction up to Ais Gill summit. Further north, the ascent of No 1848 to Beattock is shown in Table 5 which tells its own story.

Alas! not every Class 47 locomotive maintains such performances every day due to defects arising in the power equipment which are steadily being overcome. The story of the efforts to 'keep them on the road' and improve reliability is told in the next chapter.

Top right: 47.243 produces a good turn of speed while helping an ailing 50.042 on a Bristol-Paddington express as it approaches Maidenhead on 3 August 1976. / P. D. Hawkins

Right: All is far from well with D1956 as it attempts to start a Birmingham train from Carlisle on 19 September 1970. A sister locomotive was eventually summoned to replace it. / R. J. Farrell

10 Keeping them on the Road

The vast majority of passengers travelling on a locomotive-hauled train only become consciously aware of the locomotive when they are told by an embarrassed guard that it has failed. A minority of the passengers, a little more railway minded, will have read of the construction of locomotives and of the contribution made to their working by individual components. They will also have read books about footplate experiences and locomotive performance. Because the work involved is frequently far from glamorous, little seems to have been written about what goes towards 'keeping them on the road', once locomotives have been built and delivered for traffic working. In fact, the story of how control did eventually find a diesel locomotive for the 7.45am Bristol train after a string of failures can be every bit absorbing a tale as that of the crew of a hard-pressed rundown 4-4-0 steam engine flogging its way up to Ais Gill.

From early days, steam locomotives underwent regular programmed running shed maintenance which covered, amongst other things, boiler washouts and examination of valves, pistons and motion. In between these programmed attentions, other faults cropped up, many of which could be dealt with on the spot by a fitter or boilersmith. If the repair was one which by its nature could not be tackled immediately and no suitable alternative locomotive was available to work the train, a studied psychological approach by the fitters, boilersmith or chargeman to the driver would often result in the latter taking the engine after all.

An example of the above is afforded by a driver at one depot who complained that leaking tubes on his engine after the fire had been cleaned were threatening to extinguish what fire remained. The boilersmith, sent by the chargeman to examine the tubes looked at the black patch in the fire and said, 'Get her blowing off and keep her there, she'll be okay.' She was; the engine worked the trip and the return one. Steam men will know why.

Since dieselisation and electrification, locomotives have continued to receive preventive maintenance on the basis of mandatory examination schedules and to specified standards. Unfortunately skilled attention is still frequently required in between these examinations and the

Right: D1750 is engulfed by steam from a leaking steam-heating hose as it stands at Bristol Temple Meads on 8 April 1967. */ P. J. Fowler*

complex nature of diesel locomotives means that such attention can rarely be of the 'psychological' kind alone. Whereas the performance of a steam locomotive was very much influenced by the driver and fireman, who by good driving technique and sheer hard work respectively could overcome much in the way of mechanical failings, the performance of a diesel locomotive is dependent to a lesser degree on the methods of individual drivers and much more on the proper working of numerous mechanical and electrical components.

The heart of a diesel electric locomotive is, of course, the diesel engine itself, but this is useless without its associated electric generator, motors and the correct functioning of numerous contactors, relays, switches, valves, compressors, pumps and so on. Even a minor fault in any one of these can result in complete failure of the locomotive, hence the need for effective preventive maintenance.

Nor must one forget the carriage warming apparatus normally called 'the boiler' or more accurately the steam generator. Boilers are fitted to all locomotives that are normally called upon to work passenger trains (electrically heated trains are a special case of which more later). They are, nominally at any rate, fully automatic and burn diesel fuel. That means once started by the second man, the boiler should maintain steam pressure between set limits, the burner shutting off or reducing to a small flame when maximum pressure is reached, restarting again when pressure has fallen to a preset value. New coaching stock is electrically heated, however, and as already related, boilers are giving way to special alternators driven by the diesel engine, to provide electrical power via jumper cables to the coaches.

Maintenance activities in each of the five regions of BR are directed by a regional CM&EE who discharges his functions according to the administrative structure of his region. The day to day supervision of locomotive maintenance depots is exercised by area maintenance engineers or, in the case of large depots, by depot engineers. These engineers have one or more assistants responsible for day to day technical and modification matters and a number of foremen and inspectors. The foremen supervise fitters, electricians, smiths, semi-skilled and unskilled grades, and most depots work to a shift roster so that maintenance work proceeds, except for part of weekends, for 24 hours a day, seven days a week. Shift working is essential if the number of locomotives out of traffic is to be held to a minimum. If maintenance was carried out on a 9am-5pm basis only, three times as many locomotives would be out of traffic during the day time and depots would have to be much larger to accommodate a bigger fleet of locomotives.

The total number of maintenance staff employed at a depot varies according to the number of classes of locomotives allocated and the number in each class. BRs largest depot, Toton, employs a total of 342 artisan staff made up of 39 Category 1, 67 Category 2, 16 Category 3 and 190 Category 4. It has an allocation of 278 main line locomotives including 24 of Class 47. A typical medium size depot, Holbeck (Leeds) has a total allocation of 65 main line locomotives of which 15 are of Class 47.

It is not feasible in practice to allocate the more powerful main line locomotives to smaller depots since small numbers of staff cannot cope with a heavy repair influx, or carry out heavy maintenance with sufficient expedition to meet availability demands. The function of such depots is normally to carry out minor examinations and running repairs on main line diesels and to fully maintain shunting locomotives only.

The allocation of Class 47 locomotives varies with timetable requirements at any given time, but in January 1979 was as follows and is indicative of the ability of the class to operate in any terrain.

Bristol	25
Cardiff Canton	69
Gloucester	23
Landore	17
Old Oak Common	10
Total WR: 144	
Stratford	36
Tinsley	19
Immingham	25
Thornaby	14
York	28
Gateshead	19
Knottingly	15
Healey Mills	3
Finsbury Park	14
Total ER: 173	
Crewe	85
Toton	25
Bescot	47
Total LMR: 157	
Eastfield (Glasgow)	16
Haymarket (Edinburgh)	18
Total ScR: 34	
Total: 508*	

* Total includes 47/6 nominally at Tinsley but now in works for conversion to 47/9.

It will be noted that no Class 47s are allocated to depot south of the River Thames, although many frequentl work trains to the South East and southern parts c England.

A major part is played by the Crewe locomotive work of BREL which undertake the major scheduled overhaul on Class 47 locomotives as well as unscheduled repairs t severe collision damage and major component fault beyond the capability of regional depots. A Class 4 normally visits Crewe Works approximately every thre years for scheduled repairs involving removal an overhaul of all major components including the dies engine, main and auxiliary generators, compressor exhausters, boilers, traction motor blowers and bogie About 50% of BREL's Crewe Works staff is normal employed on Class 47 overhauls. Crewe Works also supplies stores and maintenance depots with overhauled spare components and other spare parts for these locomotives.

Two other important functions are involved in diesel maintenance probably more so with Class 47s than some other types of large diesel locomotives. The first of these is locomotive maintenance control whose job it is to see that locomotives are allocated to trains in such a way that the locomotives will reach their own depots when they are due for major examinations and to ensure that they receive minor examinations when they fall due wherever they may be. The locomotive maintenance control also ensures that any relevant details of an irregular performance of a locomotive or other significant incidents reach the owning depot quickly. This control operates either at regional headquarters level or alongside and as part of the principal traffic control centre of a division. Maintenance control centres are manned by engineers able to decide quickly how a particular locomotive shall be dealt with and are instrumental in preventing the build up of a number of locomotives overdue for scheduled examinations.

The other function essential to good maintenance is that performed by BR's Scientific Services Division, which is directly responsible to the CM&EE (BRB) for carrying out regular tests on diesel engine lubricating oil samples from all main line locomotives. The object of these tests is to ensure that lubricating oil contained in the diesel engine system is in a satisfactory condition. If it is not and the analysis of samples shows that oil has fallen below satisfactory levels of viscosity or detergency, or has become contaminated or exceeds a predetermined dirt content, then the owning depot is advised and arrangements are made to change the oil and, if necessary, determine the source of contamination.

As emphasised earlier in this chapter, scheduled examinations have been carried out on locomotives since the early days of railways. It may be noted that the term 'examination' in this context includes that works which a motor car owner would call servicing. It is important that the reasons for these schedules are understood as they form the bible of any locomotive maintenance organisation and the justification for maintenance depots whether for steam, diesel of electric motive power.

The first and foremost reason for the schedule is to ensure the safety of the railway line. If no regular inspections were carried out, of the bogies in particular, defects might develop that could lead to ultimate derailment. The second reason is that regular inspections will by revealing incipient failures prevent locomotive breakdowns in service with their dire effects on punctuality and customer relations. The third reason is that of minimising maintenance costs. If incipient faults are not discovered early in their development expensive damage may result to component parts of the locomotive. For example, if the carbon brushes on the main generator are not replaced when worn to a certain length, a repair bill probably in excess of £5,000 can easily result from commutator and/or flashover damage. Again, a viscosity test on a lubricating oil sample may reveal the presence of

fuel oil, probably because of a faulty fuel injector, which if not located and replaced, could result in a bearing or piston seizure and consequent damage to the cylinder block amounting to £10,000.

The formation of realistic maintenance schedules is only achieved by trial and error after a careful consideration of operating experience. When the first batches of existing classes of diesel locomotives were delivered to BR, the various component manufacturers recommended the frequency at which various items of their equipment should be examined. Such advice was based on experience with equipment elsewhere, possibly overseas, or in some cases amounted to calculated estimates by designers with generous regard for the upkeep of their own products, whether really required or not.

In the case of the Class 47 locomotives several manufacturers were involved, in particular Sulzer, Brush, Davies and Metcalfe, Spanner, Stones and BR themselves. In the early years of the Class 47s, therefore, the schedules laid down by the BRB amounted to instructions requiring attention at approximately the manufacturers recommended frequencies. For particular purposes it was necessary to group together inspections of different components at compromise periodicities, in order to simplify the schedules and avoid the need for locomotives to be stopped for attention more often than necessary. In a nutshell, it is better to examine five items every 10 days and four every 40 days than two every seven days, and three every 11 days, one every 21 days, two every 35 days and the last item every 44 days!

Since the locomotives were commissioned, maintenance schedules have been continuously reviewed in the light of experience and modifications made to equipment with the object of prolonging maintenance periods, thus reducing to a minimum locomotive time lost to the operator. In deciding the schedules a number of factors must be taken into account and balanced one against the other. On the face of things, more frequent inspections should reveal incipient faults earlier and prevent failures, but in many cases unavoidable interference with a component during inspection may make for failures, and excessively frequent inspection leads often to familiarity breeding contempt, such that defects may be overlooked by the artisan. It is here that engineering expertise is required to make a balanced judgement on all known facts. On the other hand, if the period between inspections is excessive, developing faults will more often lead to expensive failures. Lastly, the more time spent on maintenance, the more money is spent on labour and paying for additional locomotives to cover for those out of service.

Experience indicates that the best results are generally obtained from a really thorough examination carried out at relatively infrequent intervals rather than a cursory examination made more frequently. This applies particularly to electrical equipment, little of which is examined at intervals of less than 500 hours in service. Safety requirements demand frequent and thorough examination of bogies, including wheels, brake rigging and frames and also basic operational tests on the brakes.

Regional practices vary slightly but these items receive attention approximately every three days, together with a general examination of the interior of the locomotive for air, oil or coolant leakage together with a check on the diesel engine oil and coolant levels (the engine sump holds 154 gallons of oil).

The current schedule is briefly summarised below.

Details of Exams

Code	Frequency	Examples of work
A	2-4 days	as above
B	250 hours	as for A and more comprehensive brake tests. Bogie greasing check.
C	500 hours	as for B and electrical machine and control inspection. Change engine filters. Clean bogies.
D	2,000 hours	as for C plus changing of diesel engine injectors and tappet adjustment.
E	4,000 hours	as for D plus other items.

At present although all regions maintain locomotives to the above schedule as a minimum requirement, different methods are used to summate the time a locomotive spends in traffic, in order to assess when an examination is due.

Eventually all systems of calculating when the next examination is due will be superseded by TOPS, the Total Operations Processing System, originally developed by the Southern Pacific Railway in the USA and in process of being installed by BR in this country. A London based central computer will be fed with details of the activities of each locomotive and will in return declare when each locomotive is due for examination and the nature thereof.

It is interesting now to consider how a depot completes say, a 'D' examination, on a Class 47 locomotive once the maintenance control has got it to a depot. Before the examination commences, the locomotive will be moved to a special berth were the bogies will be cleaned of oil and dirt. Variously, steam, hot water and cold water at high pressure are employed for cleaning. The use of emulsifying chemicals is now generally forbidden because of the danger of pollution.

After cleaning, the locomotive will be moved to a berth within the maintenance depot where it will first receive an initial examination by a mechanical inspector. The object of this initial inspection is to reveal major faults so that the deployment of fitters, electricians and other staff can be planned to achieve rapid completion of repairs, and a check may be made to ensure that any spare components needed are available at the depot. If any part is not available a special procedure will come into play to secure a quick delivery of the part from Crewe Works, known as the 'Urgent Vehicle Standing' (UVS) procedure.

Once the initial examination is completed and the repair book carried on the locomotive has been checked to see if a driver has reported any fault, the senior shift foreman, who already knows for how much time the remainder of the examination itself should occupy his staff, will be able to assess the man-hours which repairs arising from the examination will absorb and will then plan the work so that the locomotive will be made available for traffic again as soon as possible. If the work is to be completed quickly, as many men as possible must be allocated to work on the locomotives consistent with them not getting in each other's way.

At many depots, the examination schedules are separated into 'blocks' of work, each with standard time allowance. This means that the foremen know when to expect the work to be completed and the artisan knows when the foreman will expect him to be available for another job. These 'block' times are often linked to incentive schemes of payment for work done.

As the examination proceeds, other items requiring attention will be revealed. For example, carbon brushes in motors or generators may need renewing, contactor tips may require changing, a cylinder head injector tube may be found leaking. The major faults experienced with Class 47 locomotives will be discussed later in this chapter. The actual time spent out of service in the depot by the locomotive will depend on the category of examination (an E examination takes three or four times as long as a C) and the repairs found to be required. If no major repairs are necessary, a 'C' examination can be completed in 12 hours and an 'E' in 48 hours, although heavy repair work may extend these times to two days and five days respectively, or in exceptional circumstances, even more. To minimise loss of availability as far as possible, although still complying with safety requirements, major repairs are carried out only when the locomotives is stopped for a 'D' or 'E' examination, but in practice it is necessary frequently to undertake extensive repair work at 'C' examinations.

The emphasis directed towards achieving good availability is particularly noticeable at depots whose Class 47 locomotives work predominantly on passenger trains. This class is generally in short, rather than generous supply and if a locomotive is not turned out quickly, the maintenance foreman is certain to be phoned by an anxious controller who complains that he has no motive power in sight for the 14.15 train because number 47.430 has just failed with flat batteries and will he (the foreman) please say when number 47.458 will be ready?

In about one hour, number 47.430 will be hauled into the shed, probably to join a couple of other Class 47 which are not undergoing routine examinations, but are stopped for repairs to their boilers. Needless to say, this pair should (had they remained in diagram), have been hauling trains somewhere, but to run *their* trains locomotive control has had to appropriate one Class 47 that should have come into the depot for examination, as well as another that probably should have been returned to another region which has been demanding its return for some time.

The fact that all does not proceed to plan and that locomotives do have to have out-of-course repairs delay scheduled examination work, as staff have to be taken off programmed work to attend to minor repairs requiring immediate attention. A heavy workload of unplanned repairs of this sort will mean that locomotives planned for

Right: Depot equipment for routine testing of engine lubricating oil. On the right, viscometer and heating bath; on the left, water content test bath.

Below: Combined cooling water, fuel supply and lubricating oil priming pump set. The commutator cover has been removed for access to the brush gear for maintenance.

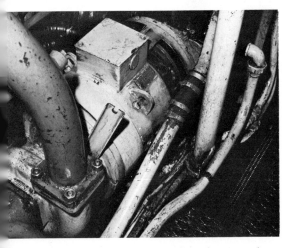

maintenance must remain in service for a few more days, until others have been released for traffic. Such locomotives will continue to receive 'A' examinations so that the needs of safety continued to be met.

Engine lubricating oil is tested, at 'B' examination frequency and the tests themselves introduce an element of uncertainty. Basic tests take place at the depot where the oil is checked for viscosity and water content while more searching tests are carried out at the nearest laboratory of the Scientific Services Division (see top photo).

Presence of water in the lubricating oil will signal the need for a thorough investigation as to its source and this may take more than 24 hours. Low viscosity is caused by the presence of fuel oil in the lubricating oil and on a Class 47 locomotive usually arises from a faulty fuel injector. Laboratory spectographic tests can determine the presence of metal particles in minute quantities, arising from an incipient bearing fault or piston seizure. Again, location of the defect can be a protracted business,

although both bearing and piston failures are fortunately comparatively rare.

One of the problem areas which has given rise to much 'out of course' attention with resultant loss of availability, is that involving the engine cooling system. The engine water and lubricating oil cooling system on the Class 47 is designed to maintain a closely-controlled level of coolant (water) temperature and is rather more sophisticated than is found in some other BR locomotives. The locomotive layout necessitated the optimum utilisation of space which led to the adoption of twin radiator fans driven, in the first 20 locomotives, by two 27hp dc electric motors, fed from the dc train heating generators. In subsequent locomotives, the train heating generator was omitted and as an alternative to low-voltage motors fed from the auxiliary generator, which was now somewhat overloaded, it was decided to use a hydrostatic drive consisting of one engine-driven pump and two hydrostatic fan motors thermostatically controlled. This arrangement proved much more effective in maintaining the engine at a constant temperature than the direct engine driven method.

The hydrostatic system is compact, but operates at high line pressures (1,500-2,000lb/sq in) using oil as the transmitting medium. Troubles emanate chiefly from leakage at pipe joints and seals which can be very messy not to mention damaging to any air brake or electrical equipment on which it is deposited.

It is worth recalling that the Sulzer LDA28 engines have no engine-driven cooling water pumps, water circulation being by means of a constant speed electric motor-driven pump set which also incorporates the engine fuel feed and lubricating oil priming (auxiliary) pump. The pump set (known usually as the 'triple-pump') is vulnerable to oil-laden dirt which can build up from leaks in the hydrostatic system as well as leaking shaft seals, etc, and can be a source of failure if not kept scrupulously clean and in good order (see photo left).

However, the greatest source of out-of-course attention is the leakage of coolant from hoses, pipe joints and other connections. One of the most troublesome is the small rubber transition bush sandwiched between the top of the cylinder block and the underside of the cylinder head. Of the simplest possible design it has to exist in a hot, oily environment under varying degrees of compression and its life is too short for it to last with certainty from one major overhaul in main works to the next. A new form of transition bush has been developed incorporating a spring-loaded rubber sleeve to allow greater longitudinal freedom of movement and is now being introduced (see photo below).

Many hose connections are required to couple pipes which move relatively to one another and these are traditionally secured by screw clips as on the motor car engine, although of considerably larger size, but here again they are not entirely satisfactory. Some are now being replaced by solid couplings of an advanced design, the necessary flexibility being provided by rubber 'O'-rings.

There are other areas where leakage occurs, notably the joint between cylinder liner and block and around the core plug in the cylinder head (the plug screws into a hole required during the original casting process) and at fractures which occur in the water jacket casing of the turbo-pressure charger. The latter two sources of leakage have resulted from a phenomenon known as thermal fatigue, brought about when a highly stressed section of metal, hot on one side and comparatively cool on the other, is subjected to alternate heating and cooling cycles. In both cases, a change of design which reduced the stress in the material is incorporated in replacement components (see bottom left photo).

Blockage of the engine lubrication oil filters can reduce engine oil pressure to a level at which a protective device operates to stop the engine. In order to render the system less sensitive to extended periods between filter changes, often the result of out-of-course attention, a substitute filter of greater capacity is being tried to extend the period between which filters have to be cleaned or changed.

The more powerful the locomotive, the more highly rated is the electrical equipment if size and weight are to be kept to a minimum. Over-heating problems quite frequently occur and affect the main generator, traction motors and main power contactors and can arise either from poor connections (with currents up to 8,000A, a connection only slightly below 'par' can, due to its increased electrical resistance, result in the generation of intense heat), lack of cooling resulting probably from a build-up of dirt in cooling ducts, or insulation breakdown, often itself the result of high temperatures — a vicious circle which has to be broken. The enormous heat generated by an electrical fault often damages adjacent equipment and cables and an extensive burn-out usually means a Main Works repair. Fortunately, the provision of well-designed fire extinguishing equipment limits the damage, but even so repairs can be expensive and protracted.

A damaging phenomenon which can affect any commutator-type electrical machine is 'flashover'. A flashover is the passage of an electric current through an arc drawn between positive and negative terminals, or more usually in an electrical machine, the brushboxes or one brushbox and the carcase of the machine. A flashover develops when sparking at current collectors (brushes) occurs and the surrounding air becomes ionised providing an easier path for the current than through the machine. Conductive dirt inside a machine operating at high voltage can also provide an alternative current path and flashover again results. In practice, a short current interruption caused by a set of brushes momentarily leaving the commutator when travelling at high speed (and with high applied voltage) or the similar effect due to failure of the control system to adjust rapidly enough during wheelslip, can result in flashover. The heat in the arc can cause considerable damage leading to heavy repairs. Whilst a minor flashover may only cause sooting of the machine, which can be cleaned up, a severe flashover can result in complete failure of the locomotive and a Main Works repair (see photos right and above right).

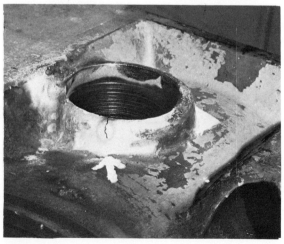

Above left: Dowty water transition bushes (cylinder block to head); latest type in front.

Left: Cylinder head showing crack starting from core plug hole.

The overriding need during the design of the Class 47 locomotives to limit individual axleloads and hence overall weight led to weight-reducing measures in all parts of the equipment, one of which was the engine starting battery, the capacity of which was cut to the minimum. The original batteries would permit only four successive starts of a cold engine before becoming discharged to a point at which firing speed was unattainable. The engine is not normally difficult to start, but unless sufficient time for the batteries to recoup is allowed between successive starts then difficulty is experienced. Batteries of large capacity are now being fitted as replacements become necessary (see photo bottom right).

As regular winter-time passengers came to realise only too well in the early days of dieselisation, adequate steam heating of trains tended to be a spasmodic luxury. Although in the days of steam locomotives, it could never be claimed that there were not shortcomings in train heating systems which came to light if the winter was more severe than average, the means of generating steam for heating rarely failed, since the locomotive boiler supplied it, only the means of conveying it to the passenger. This was due to burst, leaking or frozen hose pipes, a defective reducing valve on the locomotive or a driver/fireman who became niggardly with the steam supply if the engine was steaming badly.

Of the three different types of steam carriage warming apparatus in present use within the Class 47 fleet, two are now classed as steam generators, the third being a more conventional fire-tube boiler of the dry-back type. All three are designed to operate automatically once started up and herein lies the root of their troubles since almost all the faults are caused either by safety devices (an example is the one intended to stop the fuel supply in case of non-ignition) or by some part of the cycle control apparatus. For instance, the fuel supply should be cut off when steam pressure has attained a certain level but should flow again and re-ignite when steam pressure has fallen to a certain lower level; but a faulty steam pressure-switch may prevent restarting. A surprising number of failures result from inability to transfer water from the underframe storage tank to the fire tube boiler itself without creation of air-locks.

All three varieties of steam raising equipment are known to have given consistently reliable performances in stationary applications over long periods. The fact that so many failures occur when they are installed in locomotives seems to imply that a steel wheel running on a steel rail gives rise to destructive frequencies of vibration which cause delicate mechanisms to fail. Yet much has been done in the way of modifications to pipework and fuel and electrical systems and things are significantly better today. A volume could be written on faults which have caused in-traffic failures. However, more than 10 years' of experience and modifications have done much to eliminate the common causes of casualties and a high proportion of today's delays result from seemingly random failures of pipes (air, oil fuel), seals and diaphragms (air) and electrical equipment (contacts, wiring, switches). Although all diesel locomotives are

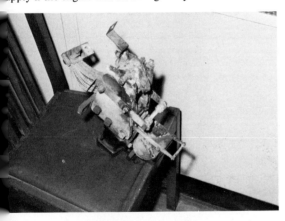

Left: Electrical equipment fault damage.

Below left: Traction motor brush box damaged by flashover.

Below: Engine starting battery, one four-cell unit (12 per locomotive).

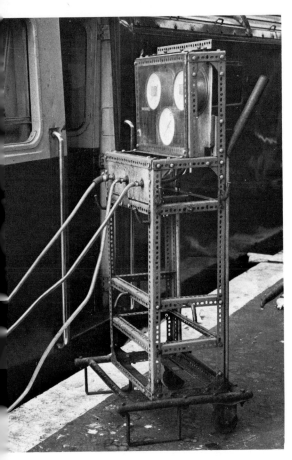

Left: Air and vacuum brake test in progress.

Above: Air and vacuum brake test stand.

equipped with straight air brakes acting on the locomotive only, they have to control vacuum braked trains. Many of them are equipped also to control air-braked trains and most of the Class 47 are so fitted.

Safe train operation requires the locomotive to apply a retarding force proportional to that applied by the train brakes, and in the case of partially-fitted freight trains, a little before the train brakes have been applied, so that the train can be 'gathered together' gently behind the locomotive. The locomotive brakes can be set to deal correctly with different types of trains (air-passenger, air-goods, vacuum-passenger, vacuum-goods) by the movement of a 4-way selector switch.

It is equally important to be able to release the brakes as rapidly as possible and the brake system includes special features to effect the rapid releases of air or vacuum brakes. In addition to the brake test carried out on the Class 47s at least once every four days, a more comprehensive test is made at the 'B' examination and any deviations in pressure settings receive attention. In practice frequent attention is found to be necessary to the

rapid release equipment provided for air-braked trains. The brake system is designed to fail safe and, furthermore, any incipient faults will often be found by a driver as he carries out preparation duties on the locomotive before it works a train (see accompanying photos).

Probably the outstandingly successful system on the Class 47 locomotives is that catering for the diesel engine load control and traction motor field diversion. The system ensures that the diesel engine's available power output can be effectively used to attain the desired road speed as quickly as possible. Although the system is complex compared with the corresponding systems on most other types of diesel locomotive, it gives excellent results, good reliability and a welcome absence from the power surge problems that affect more than half of the remaining diesel-electrics in the BR fleet.

On certain Class 47 locomotives electronic equipment replaces electromagnetic relays and resistances and although some teething troubles have been experienced, partially because electronic equipment needs careful protection from the Spike voltages arising from electromagnetic equipment, its increasing reliability bodes well for the future.

It must not be inferred from the difficulties outlined in this chapter that the Class 47s have no redeeming features from the maintenance man's view point. They have many. In certain aspects of design and operation, the Class 47s are much more satisfactory than most other diesel locomotives. In particular, they do not suffer from power surge (the electrical and engine load control system prevents this) or fuel dilution, the term used to cover the contamination of the engine lubricating oil by fuel oil which arises generally from leaks from fuel pipe joints on the engine itself — something which afflicts most other designs of diesel engine. It is hoped, however, that sufficient has been set down relating to day-to-day maintenance work to indicate the complexity of the task of keeping a large fleet of locomotives on the move .

With the increasing age of the fleet, it is to be expected that other defects will develop which will need ever more comprehensive overhauls and renewal of components in order to enable the prime movers to continue to function with reasonable mechanical efficiency. An example of this is afforded when, say, an exhaust valve spindle breaks above the head which later then becomes trapped between cylinder head and piston.

Before the engine is stopped, the piston crown may have taken a heavy battering resulting in its disintegration. Small pieces of aluminium alloy and cast iron may pass into the exhaust pipes and thence into the turbo-charger with resultant damage to the blades. Alternatively, the valve head may be forced into the cylinder head water space, permitting coolant to fill the cylinder (and maybe other cylinders). When this happens, the engine is stopped suddenly by hydraulic lock with almost inevitable bending of connecting rods.

With all of this in mind and the future pattern of traffic now becoming evident British Railways have just embarked on a Heavy General Repair programme for the whole class and this is the subject of the next chapter.

11 To the Present

As can be seen from the first chapter, the initial batch of 20 locomotives had been delivered to the Eastern Region by the middle of 1963 and the next batch followed on close behind. By the end of 1976 the mean age of the fleet was 12 out of an accountancy *life* of 20 years. Late in 1974 British Railways had decided that the Class 47 would be needed, particularly for freight work well beyond the 20 years *book* life and set out to review the work required and estimate the cost of carrying out a heavy half-life general overhaul and up-dating process on the whole fleet. The outcome was the setting up of a Heavy General Repair programme to be undertaken in Crewe Works at a rate of two locomotives per working week from which it is clear it would take just over five years from the commencement to cover the whole fleet.

At the same time it was decided that one locomotive should be rebuilt to provide a mobile test bed for the new Ruston Paxman 16RK3CT engine and 47.046 (1628) was selected as it required extensive rebuilding following collision damage. It has been reclassified 47/6 and renumbered 47.601 and is described in more detail later.

The Heavy General Repair programme — known now within BR as the HGR programme — is designed to fit the fleet for satisfactory operation into the 1990s and gives special attention to those parts of the locomotives where there are shortcomings. To this end there is an extensive programme of replacement of certain components, some of which were already highlighted in the last chapter, by new components of improved design, the intention being to bring each unit up close to *as-new* standard.

Mention can be made of only a few examples as detailed coverage would involve a book in itself. In Chapter 3, the purpose-built line-boring machine is described and this has been installed in Crewe Works where it is being used for re-boring those crankcases on which bearing saddle alignment is outside the acceptable limits. On such crankcases the bearing saddles are being bored out slightly larger than originally, to restore correct alignment and parallelism which then requires provision of bearings having a slightly larger outside diameter to suit.

Right: Named Class 47 — old style. The Western Region named several of its Class 47s after its engineers and some of its early locomotives. *North Star* was the GWR's first successful locomotive and a worthy predecessor to D1661.

In Chapter 10 cracks from cylinder head core plugs are mentioned and an example is shown (see photo p84). New cylinder heads are being provided and fitted which incorporate a number of improvements adopted from service experience and in line with up-to-date developments. There are three main differences, two of which are designed to improve cooling and stress distribution. The same kind of action has been taken with the pressure charger housing and a new and improved steel has been used for the gas inlet casing which has to withstand, even under normal conditions, what are very high temperatures of the order of 600-650°C (1,100-1,200°F).

cylinder block and heads while the secondary circuit cools the combustion air and the lubricating oil heat exchanger. The secondary circuit is maintained at a lower temperature than the primary, principally to ensure that the combustion air is cooled sufficiently to enable the induction of an adequate mass of air for the purpose of complete combustion.

British Rail (E) 47.601

To turn now to the one example of Class 47/6 locomotive 47.046 was rebuilt (and renumbered 47.601), incorporating a Ruston Paxman 16 RK3CT engine (16-cylinder Vee formation) and a Brush 3-Phase alternator, as fitted to the Class 56 freight locomotives.

Rebuilding was very extensive and included a completely new engine cooling system layout incorporating two distinct circuits. The primary circuit cools the engine

Below: The Hereford cider firm provided eye-catching decoration for 47.185 when it hauled their 'Strongbow Express' to Paddington on 5 May 1977. The locomotive was then used on empty stock duty from Paddington to Old Oak Common. / *M. Orme*

Below right: In honour of the Queen's Silver Jubilee, Stratford works painted a number of locomotives with silver roofs during 1977. Numbers 47.163/4 also received large Union Jacks, and in this condition the latter was photographed at Llandudno Junction on 11 October 1977. / *L. Goddard*

The radiator banks (one on each side for each system, four banks in all) are fitted below cantrail level, the two fans drawing air first through the secondary banks and then through the primary banks. The fans are driven by means of a Serck-Behr hydrostatic system similar to that in use on most of the Class 47 fleet. Much of the brake control equipment is situated in the space between the radiator banks and beneath the fans.

The erstwhile boiler compartment reduced in size now contains the main rectifier for supplying the DC traction motors and other electrical equipment, such as the battery charging control unit. Much of the electromagnetic control gear as fitted to the earlier Class 47 locomotives has given way to electronic equipment. Power output of the locomotive, as required by the driver, is controlled by a Woodward engine governor and a thyristor based load regulator unit.

The conventional auxiliary generator has given way to a 3-phase auxiliary alternator whose output supplies the AC compressors and traction motor blowers, and also, after rectification and voltage reduction, charges the battery. The engine is started by two Bosch starter motors, one on each side of the engine. Unlike a conventional Class 47, where the engine is motored by providing a supply from the battery to the starting winding on the main generator, it is not practicable for the alternator to motor the engine. No facilities are available for providing train heat.

The locomotive is fitted with slow speed control equipment for hauling MGR (Merry-go-round) coal trains. The equipment has detail differences from that employed on conventional Class 47 locomotives. The brake control system is a new development (similar to that fitted to the High Speed Train) and replaces the driver's air brake valve with a notched controller which, dependent on its position, sends a variable electronic signal to a pressure transducer unit. This unit maintains the automatic air train pipe pressure at the level required by the driver more accurately than can the almost entirely pneumatic system on the remainder of the Class 47 fleet.

And so one of the most ubiquitous and versatile classes of locomotive in the history of British Railways continues to take the front line in tackling any sort of traffic. It bore the brunt of the most exacting requirements for almost a decade and whatever their fate in the future, that fact will be long remembered.

Every inch of its 63ft 7in length is emphasised in this broadside view of the unique Class 47/6. This locomotive (formerly D1628) was re-engined with a Ruston Paxman 16 RK 3 CT engine of 3,250hp. / *P. D. Hawkins*

To bring the reader right up to date, let us look at what has taken place since this manuscript was first presented to the Publisher. In the first place, the special General Overhaul, known in British Railways circles as the Heavy Repair Programme, is well underway with 137 locomotives receiving the full treatment by the middle of 1978, with benefits both to availability and reliability. On the other hand there are some components which are still the cause for some concern and to which solutions have either not yet been found, or the cost of application has not been seen to produce any or sufficient saving.

Take for instance the sporadic breakage of exhaust valves. The engine manufacturer has indicated means for increasing operational safety, but as this would be at the expense of some loss of interchangeability, British Railways are reluctant to adopt the solution which, in the extreme, could lead to difficulties in the changeover period if a valve had to be changed for any reason and the wrong type happened to be available at the depot concerned. This may sound a trivial point, but on a system as big and complex as British Railways it is always possible, particularly when one considers the number of depots, not to mention main workshops on the system. But with a little more care in repair and fitting, together with a change to a material which has only recently become available, the problem is being contained.

Sometimes a modification designed to eliminate one particular problem can lead to another hitherto unsuspected problem appearing elsewhere, having been masked by the first. Such a situation has occurred with the turbochargers, where a modification to the main casing to eliminate cracks in one area led to failure in another area, because the stress in the latter zone, although previously regarded as safe, was suddenly highlighted when the first zone was given attention. As a result, the manufacturer, together with the Railway Research Department, has had to carry out an extensive test programme in order to prove a further modification and to calculate the life-expectancy of the casing in the new situation, before embarking on what is to be the final solution. In the case in point, it was found that thermal stressing of a high order was occurring which could be reduced by as much as 50% by a relatively simple machining modification, together with the provision of a heat shield and a small and simple water deflector in the cooling water space to improve water circulation by deflecting more cooling water into the heat-affected zone.

But there are other problems with which the operator is content to live, or perhaps realises that it is simpler to live with than to adopt an expensive solution. Again there is one of these situations in the turbocharger. We are now all familiar with the term Metal Fatigue, since the Comet disasters of two decades ago. As a result it is now clearly established that aluminium has a definite life, dependent upon the number of reversals of stress to which it is subjected and the level of stress. The impellor, which compresses the air for combustion runs at a very high speed, of the order of 13,000rpm, is accelerated to that speed and decelerated again many times over as the engine is operated in the course of its daily work. After some years in service, the metal suffers the effects of fatigue and cracks appear in a highly stressed area, which, if left, grow quite rapidly and if left long enough, the impellor will burst. While a different method of fixing to that now employed could cure the problem, albeit at some cost and inconvenience, the safe period of service has now been clearly established and replacement is carried out at that time, at somewhat lower cost than wholesale replacement of the total number by those of a new design which would also require modification of the shaft as well.

The advent and introduction of HSTs on both Western and Eastern Regions is changing the role performed by the Class 47s and they are now being transferred more to freight working. On the other hand a batch of locomotives is being modified to work push-pull trains, initially in the Scottish Region between Edinburgh and Glasgow where they will replace the smaller Sulzer engined Class 27s.

There is little doubt that the Class 47s are destined to be with us for many years yet. There has been talk of possible re-engining but the experience with 47.601 now being used once again to test a new prototype GEC engine of their latest type RK3A, a 12-cylinder unit this time with an output of 3,500bhp at 1,000rpm — perhaps the engine of the future for BR heavy freight locomotives, not to mention the excessively high cost of such an exercise — close to that of a new locomotive — has been set against the cost of a 'Half-Life' Overhaul such as has been, and is being carried out at Crewe in their Heavy Repair Programme at less than one-third of the cost of a new locomotive.

Railway enthusiasts all have their favourites and there are some who maintain that the Class 45s are better locomotives, giving better performances than the Class 47s, but British Railways' own statistics do not confirm this, particularly on a 'Miles per Casualty' basis — and a casualty does not get a train to its destination on time.

It is hoped that this account of the largest class of main-line locomotives on British Railways does the class justice. There is much which could possibly have been said which has had to be omitted for the sake of brevity. Possibly troubles have been highlighted rather than outstanding performances in traffic, but in the end a class of locomotive is judged by its usefulness to its operators who have to move trains at the lowest cost and it is submitted that the Class 47s are doing just that!

Above right: Pride of Stratford's fleet in early 1978 was 47.460, here seen at Norwich after its first duty in elaborate livery with white roof, and named *Great Eastern.* / *L. Bertram*

Right: Striking study of 47.052 at speed near Pilmoor on a northbound oil train on 8 May 1976. / *J. E. Oxley*

Appendix

The Class 47s

Original Loco Nos	New Loco Nos	Class	Heating	Motors	Quantity
1500-19	47.401-20	47/4	ETH (DC)	S/P	20
1520/5/7/31/3-6/41/2/5/7-9	47.421-34	47/4	ETH (AC/DC)	S/P	14
1521-4/6/8-30/2/7-40/3/4/6	47.001-16	47/0		S/P	16
1550-61/3-9/71/4	47.435/529/436-54	47/4	ETH (AC/DC)	S/P	21
1570/2/3	47.017-9	47/0		S/P	3
1575/7/8/80/1	47.455/7/8/60/1	47/4	ETH (AC/DC)	Par	5
1576/9/82	47.456/9/62	47/4	ETH (AC/DC)	Par	3
1583	47.020	47/0		Par	1
1584/5	47.531/42	47/4	ETH (AC/DC)	Par	2
1586	47.463	47/4	ETH (AC/DC)	Par	1
1587-9	47.464/543/465	47/4	ETH (AC/DC)	Par	3
1590	47.466	47/4	ETH (AC/DC)	Par	1
1591	47.024	47/0		Par	1
1592-4/6	47.544/467/8/70	47/4	ETH (AC/DC)	Par	4
1595/8	47.469/71	47/4	ETH (AC/DC)	Par	2
1597/9	47.026/7	47/0		Par	2
1600/7/8/12	47.472/7-9	47/4	ETH (AC/DC)	Par	4
1601-4	47.473-6	47/4	ETH (AC/DC)	Par	4
1605/10/13/15	47.028/31/3/5	47/0		Par	4
1606/9/11/14	47.029/30/2/4	47/0		Par	4
1616/20/1/7	47.480/4/5/481	47/4	ETH (AC/DC)	Par	4
1617-9/22-6/8-30	47.036-8/—/41-8	47/0		Par	11
1631-5	47.049-53	47/0		Par	5
1636/7/41/2/6/9/51/5/7	47.482/3/532/47/45/35/33/36/37	47/4	ETH (AC/DC)	Par	9
1638-40/3-5/7/8/50/2-4	47.054-6/59-61/3/4/6/8-70	47/0		Par	12
1656/8-61/3-8/70/2-7/9-81	47.072/4-83/5-91/3-5	47/0		Par	21
1662/9/78	—/538/534	47/4	ETH (AC/DC)	Par	3
1682/4-8/90-9	47.096-111	47/0		S/P	16
1700-6/8-12/4	47.112-124	47/0		S/P	13
1683/9	—/47.486	47/4	ETH (AC/DC)	S/P	2
1707/13	47.487/8	47/4	ETH (AC/DC)	S/P	2
1715/6/8/23-5/30/46/7	47.548/489/539/40/49/490/550/1/46	47/4	ETH (AC/DC)	Par	9
1717/20/2/6-9/31-3/5-45	47.126/9/31/4-7/9-52	47/0		Par	21
1719/21/48-52	47.128/30/55-9	47/0		Par	7
1753/60	47.491/2	47/4	ETH (AC/DC)	Par	2
1754/6/7	47.160/2/3	47/0		Par	3
1755	47.541	47/4	ETH (AC/DC)	Par	1
1758/9/61-81	47.164-86	47/0		Par	23
1782-1836	47.301-55	47/3	NB	Par	55
1837-74	47.187-224	47/0		Par	38
1875-1900	47.356-381	47/3	NB	Par	26
1901-7/9-29/31/3-5/8	47.225-52/54-8	47/0		Par	33
1930/2/6/7/9-61/8/75	47.530/493-506/552/507-11/53/4/512-7	47/4	ETH (AC/DC)	Par	29
1962-7/9-74/6	47.262-74	47/0		Par	13
1977-99, 1100	47.275-98	47/0		Par	24
1101-11	47.518-28	47/4	ETH (AC/DC)	Par	11

Total: 508

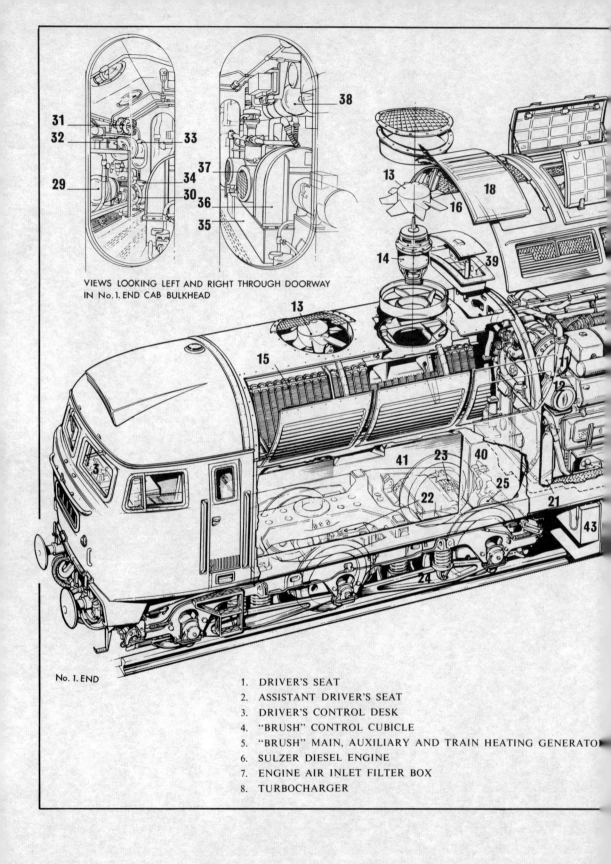

VIEWS LOOKING LEFT AND RIGHT THROUGH DOORWAY
IN No. 1. END CAB BULKHEAD

No. 1. END

1. DRIVER'S SEAT
2. ASSISTANT DRIVER'S SEAT
3. DRIVER'S CONTROL DESK
4. "BRUSH" CONTROL CUBICLE
5. "BRUSH" MAIN, AUXILIARY AND TRAIN HEATING GENERATOR
6. SULZER DIESEL ENGINE
7. ENGINE AIR INLET FILTER BOX
8. TURBOCHARGER